GCSE IN A WEEK

Gurinder Chadha, Dan Evans and John Parker

GCSE IN A WEEK

Use this day-by-day listing and the tabs on each page in the book to plan your revision.

Day		Page
1	Cells	4
1	Cell action	6
1	Photosynthesis	8
1	Human nutrition	10
1	Blood	12
1	Heart	14
1	Respiration	16
1	Nerves	18
2	Brain	20
2	Hormones	22
2	Kidneys	24
2	Homeostasis	26
2	Inheritance	28
2	Cell division	30
2	Sexual reproduction	32
2	Selective breeding	34
2	Evolution	36
3	Pollution	38
3	Nitrogen and carbon cycles	40
3	Atomic structure	42
3	Ionic bonding, ionic structures and metallic bonding	44
3	Covalent bonding and structures	46
3	Crude oil: formation and separation	48
3	Alkanes and cracking	50
3	Alkenes and polymerisation	52
4	Extraction of iron and aluminium	54
4	Copper purification and electrolysis of brine	56
4	Reversible reactions and production of ammonia	58
4	The rock cycle	60

Day		Page
4	Working out formulae	62
4	Balancing equations	64
4	Mole calculations 1	66
4	Mole calculations 2	68
5	The periodic table 1	70
5	The periodic table 2	72
5	Rates of reaction	74
5	Acids, alkalis and salts	76
5	Exothermic and endothermic reactions	78
5	Speed, velocity and acceleration	80
5	Using graphs to describe motion	82
5	Force and acceleration	84
6	Friction	86
6	Cars and stopping distances	88
6	Work done, energy and power	90
6	Types of energy	92
6	Static charge and current	94
6	Voltage and resistance	96
6	Electrical circuits	98
6	Electromagnetism and electromagnetic induction	100
7	Thermal energy transfer 1	102
7	Thermal energy transfer 2	104
7	Wave properties	106
7	Sound	108
7	Light	110
7	Radioactivity	112
7	The Earth's structure and seismic waves	114
7	Stars and the Universe	116
	Answers	118

CELLS

DAY 1

A cell is the smallest unit of life. Some organisms, such as the amoeba, consist of just one cell.

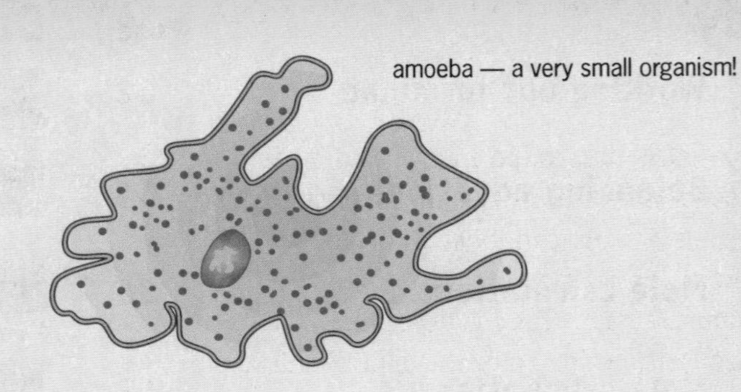

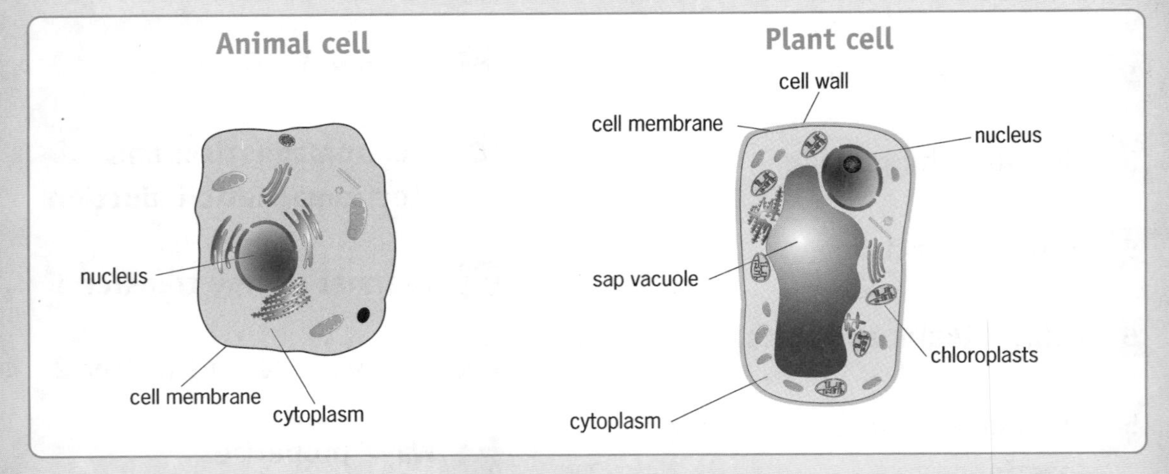

Look at the table below. Note the similarities and differences between animal and plant cells.

Do all plant cells contain chloroplasts?

	Animal cells		Plant cells
Similarities		**both** have a cell membrane	
		both have a nucleus	
		both have cytoplasm	
Differences	have no cell wall		have a cell wall
	have no chloroplasts		have chloroplasts
	have no sap vacuole		have a sap vacuole

What is the biggest organism in the world? Not a whale! It is the giant redwood of California.

Different cells do different jobs

Every cell is controlled by a **nucleus**, is enclosed by a **membrane** and has semi-fluid **cytoplasm**. Cells can exist in a number of different forms, e.g. there are blood cells and muscle cells. Each type of cell has a specific function, e.g. red blood cells carry oxygen.

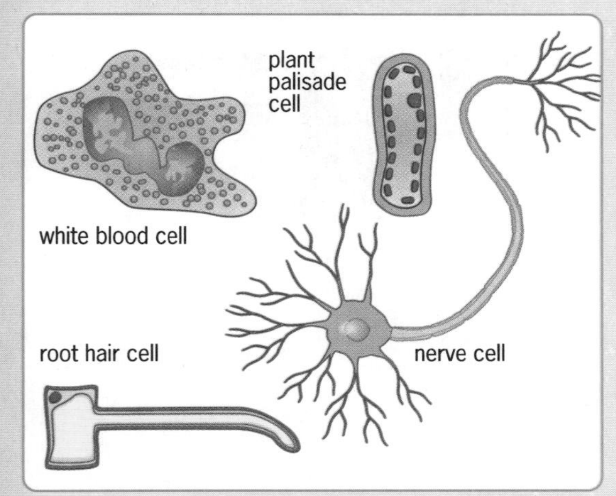

These cells are working together in a trachea (windpipe).

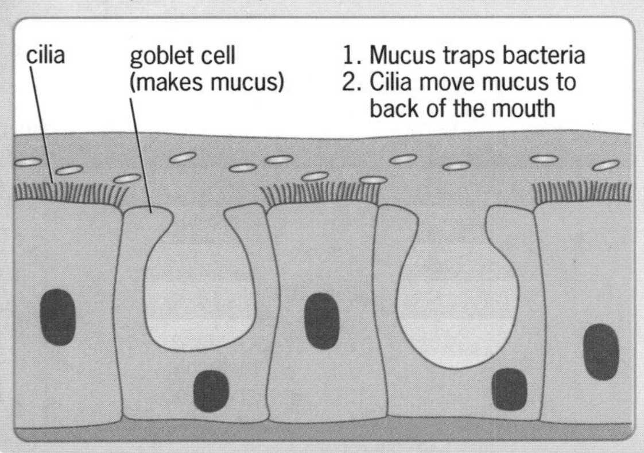

Progress check

1. Which structures are found in both animal and plant cells?
   nucleus, cytoplasm, membrane
2. Which structures are found in both a plant palisade cell and a root hair cell? membrane, nucleus, cytoplasm, sap vacuole, cell wall
3. Name the structure that controls a cell.
   nucleus
4. What is the function of the cilia on the cells that line the trachea (windpipe)?
   move the mucus through the windpipe
5. Smoking destroys the cilia along the trachea. What effect would this have on the lungs?
   The lungs could become full of mucus leading to infections such as bronchitus

CELL ACTION

Jamie Oliver needs a supply of ingredients to create a meal. In the same way, a cell needs a supply of useful substances, e.g. oxygen, glucose. Exit of some substances is also important. The cell membrane is selective!

Diffusion

Diffusion is the movement of molecules from a **high concentration** to a **low concentration**.

Diffusion takes place only with gases and liquids! Molecules have kinetic energy and move randomly in all directions. They spread out so as to become evenly dispersed everywhere.

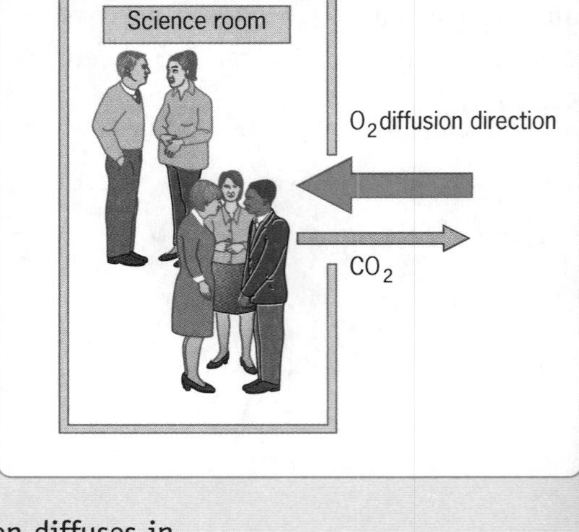

- In a room people use up the oxygen in respiration.
- This results in a low concentration inside the room but a high concentration outside the room.
- Because of the concentration difference, oxygen diffuses in.

Can you work out why carbon dioxide diffuses out?

Osmosis: the movement of water through the cell membrane

Osmosis is the movement of **just** water molecules. The water molecules move from a **lower concentrated solution** to a **higher concentrated solution** through a partially permeable membrane. (If you miss out the word 'solution' you will miss out on the marks!)

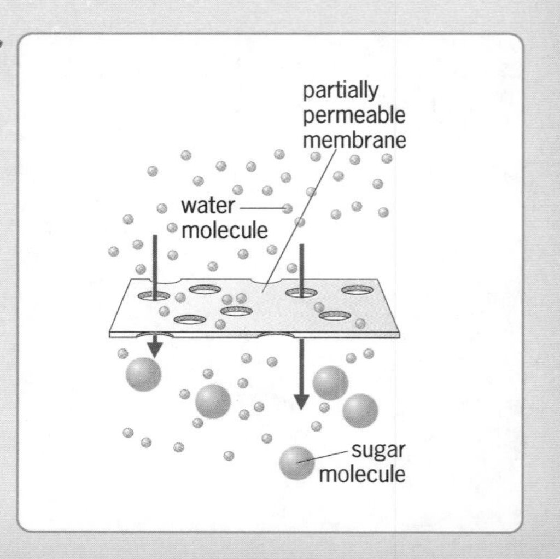

Another way to look at it: water molecules move from where they are in higher concentration to where they are in lower concentration.

Inside a living cell many reactions take place. The cell membrane protects against entry of toxic substances and the escape of internal structures and substances.

A root hair takes in water by osmosis:

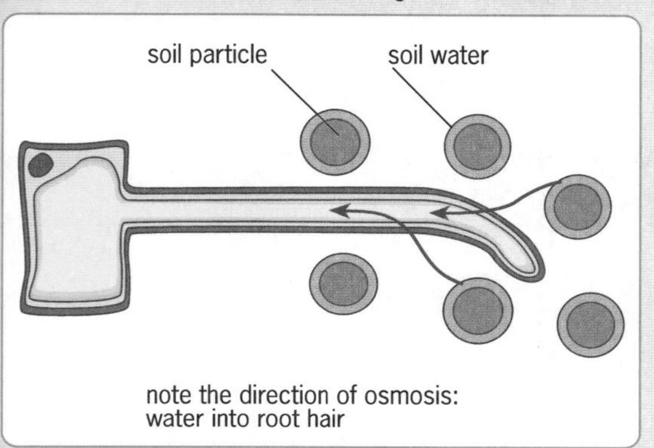

- The cell membrane is selectively permeable.
- The soil water is a less concentrated solution.
- The cell sap is a more concentrated solution.

Active transport

Molecules move from where they are in **lower concentration** to where they are in **higher concentration** through a cell membrane. This needs **energy** released during respiration and special transporter molecules in the membrane.

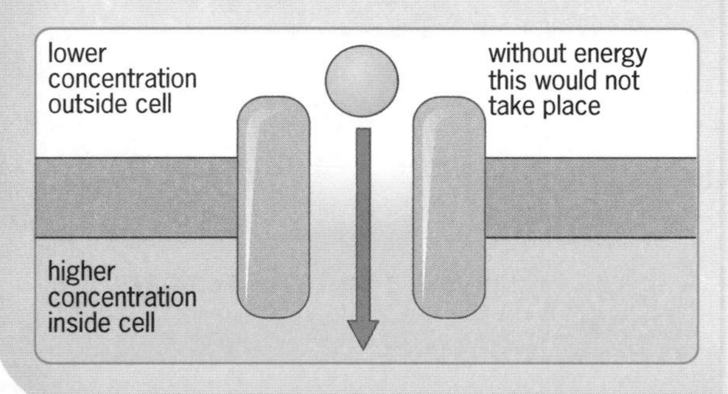

Progress check

Tick the statement if it is true and cross it if it is not.

Statement	Diffusion	Osmosis	Active transport
Molecules move from high to low concentration	✓	✓	✗
Molecules move from low to high concentration	✗	✗	✓
Water molecules move through a partially permeable membrane	✗	✓	✗
Passage of molecules through a membrane needs energy	✗	✗	✓
Molecules move down a concentration gradient	✓	✓	✗

PHOTOSYNTHESIS

10 MINS

DAY 1

All green plants can make some glucose, even grass and weeds. Plants provide the starting point for consumer organisms.

Why is a leaf like a sugar factory?

The diagram shows a section through a leaf. Only cells with **chloroplasts** carry out the process of photosynthesis. Can you detect the three types of cell that contain chloroplasts? Chloroplasts produce lots of glucose, a sugar full of stored chemical energy.

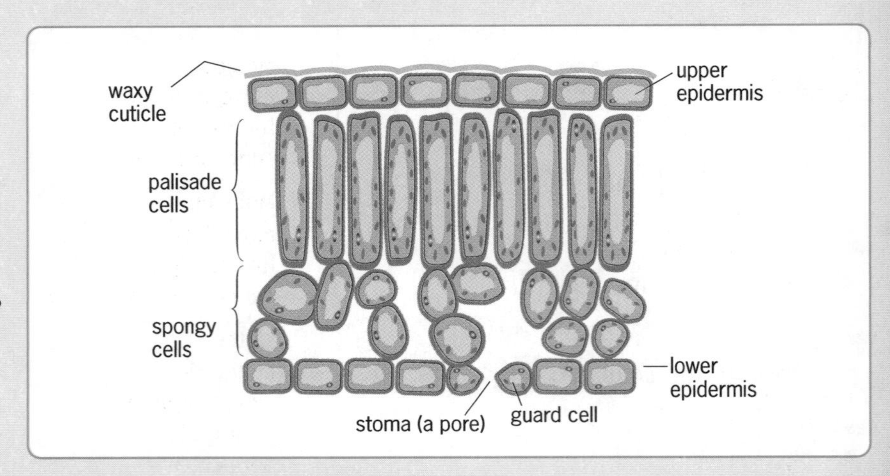

What is photosynthesis?

needs suitable temperature

water + **carbon dioxide** → **glucose** + **oxygen**

needs light
needs chloroplasts

Photosynthesis can take place only in suitable conditions. **Light** and a **suitable temperature** are vital to the process!

Which plants supply great yields of glucose? Many food plants do this, with sugar beet and sugar cane at number 1 in the production charts.

Task: the plant detectives

How can we find out if a leaf has been photosynthesising?

A plant converts a lot of glucose to starch. If you can detect starch in a leaf, you have proved that a plant has been photosynthesising!

- Glucose is soluble and this helps with **transport**.
- Starch is insoluble and this helps with **storage**.

How do we test a leaf for starch?

- Dip the leaf in boiling water.
- Boil the leaf in ethanol in an electric water bath to remove the cuticle and chlorophyll.
- Dip the leaf in hot water to re-hydrate.
- Dip the whole leaf in iodine solution.
- If the leaf contains starch it goes a blue-black colour.

Progress check

1. Which gas is needed for photosynthesis?

   Carbon dioxide

2. Which gas is given off during photosynthesis?

   oxygen

3. Describe suitable conditions for photosynthesis.

   light
   suitable temp.

HUMAN NUTRITION

The digestive system

mouth – breaks food up into small pieces giving high surface area for enzymes to work efficiently

oesophagus – passes food to stomach

stomach – contains hydrochloric acid and helps break down protein

liver – makes bile

pancreas – helps break down fats and oils, proteins and starch

gall bladder – stores bile

small intestine – absorbs small soluble food molecules, e.g glucose

large intestine – absorbs water

Peristalsis

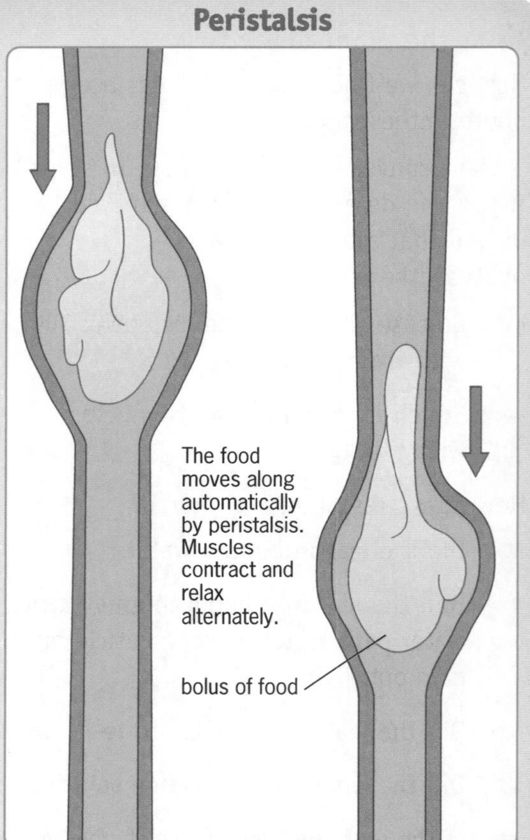

How do enzymes work?

- All enzymes have an **active site**.
- A **substrate** molecule binds to the active site, forming an **enzyme–substrate complex.**
- The substrate is broken down into **smaller molecules**.
- All enzymes are **specific**, only breaking down certain substrate molecules.
- Once the substrate has been broken down then the enzyme is **ready for use again**.

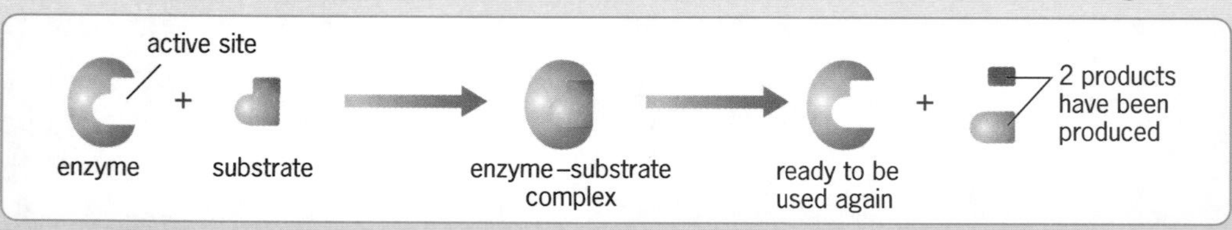

Digestive juices break down large food molecules into molecules small enough to be absorbed into the bloodstream.

Which conditions affect enzyme-controlled reactions?

- At **optimum temperature** (37 °C) the rate of reaction is best.
- Below **optimum temperature** the rate of reaction begins to slow down, and at very low temperatures the enzymes become inactive.
- Above **optimum temperature** reactions also begin to slow down, and at very high temperatures the enzymes become inactive (denatured).
- At **optimum pH** the rate of reaction is best.
- Above or below **optimum pH** the rate of reaction is slower.

Digestion

The digestive juice **saliva** contains **amylase** (a type of **carbohydrase**), which begins the breakdown of starch into sugar. This is followed by **gastric juice**, produced in the stomach, which contains **pepsin** (a type of **protease**). This breaks down proteins into amino acids. Pepsin needs acid to work effectively. **Pancreatic juice** produces more carbohydrases, proteases and **lipases**, which break down fats and oils into fatty acid and glycerol. The liver makes **bile**, which neutralises the stomach acid and allows the enzymes in the small intestine to work.

Progress check

Analyse the graph, which shows two enzyme-controlled reactions.

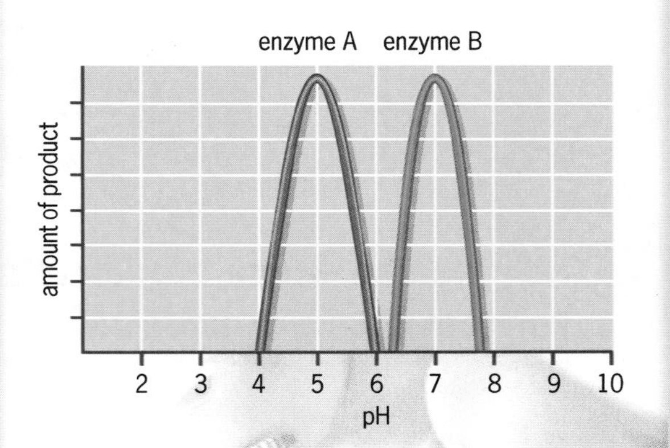

1. a) Which enzyme, A or B, works best in acid conditions? A
   b) Suggest which enzyme it is.
   ~~Bile~~ Pepsin

2. What would happen to these enzymes:
   a) at a very high temperature? denature
   b) at a very low temperature? slow down rate of reaction (inactive)

BLOOD

What is in the blood?

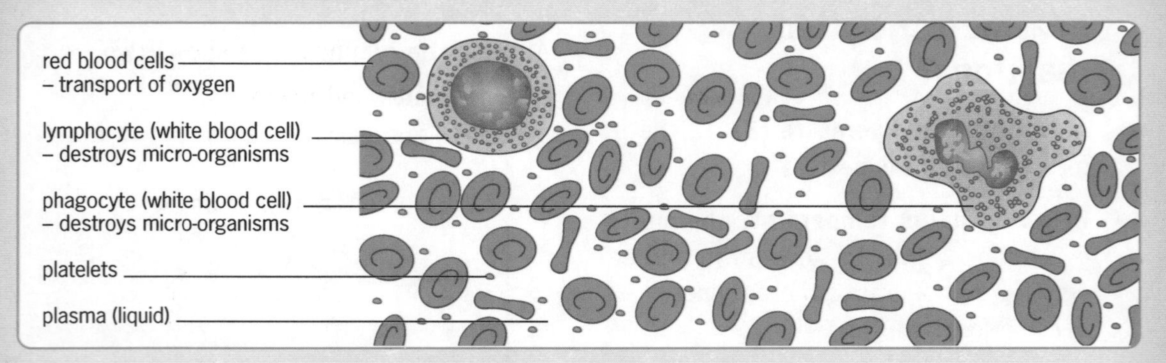

How do the white blood cells protect us from micro-organisms?

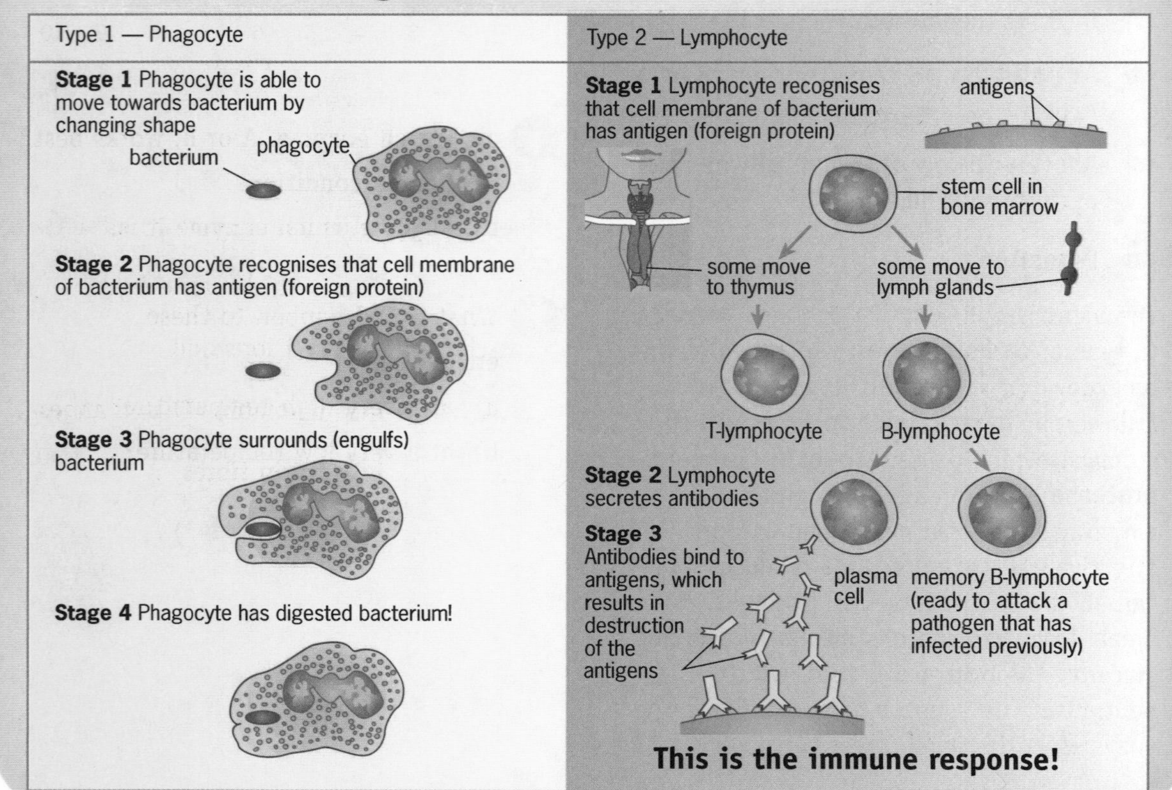

Blood is moved around the body in blood vessels. It transports a wide range of substances and defends against invasion by micro-organisms.

Red blood cells

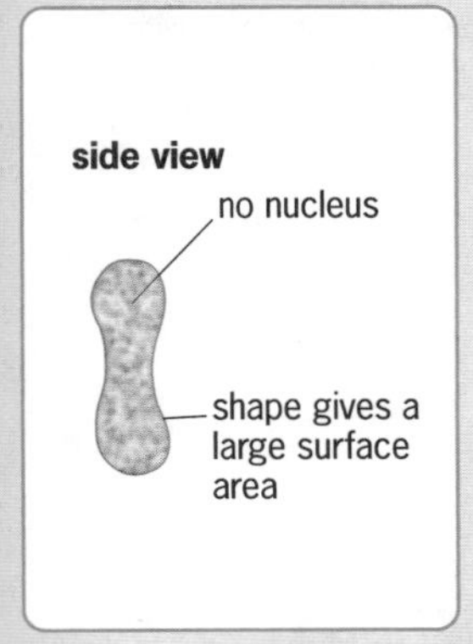

- Red blood cells have a biconcave shape – this gives the cell a high surface area to volume ratio, so more oxygen is carried.
- Red blood cells have haemoglobin – this gives **affinity** (attraction) for oxygen.
- Over 90% of the volume of the red cell is haemoglobin so lots of oxygen can be carried.

Iron is needed in our diet to make haemoglobin.

Blood clots

It is vital that the blood clots:

- to prevent blood loss
- to prevent micro-organism entry into the bloodstream

Platelets help blood to clot.

Progress check

Follow this diagram to see the many factors needed to make blood clot. Then complete the passage below by filling in the gaps.

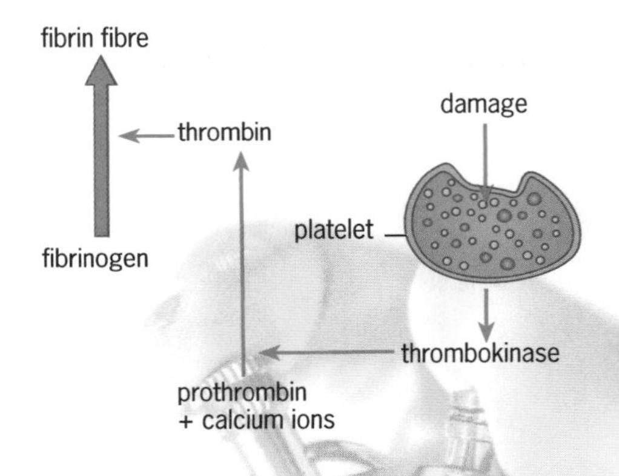

When the vessel is damaged the platelets produce ...thrombo... This is an enzyme that converts calcium ions and ...prothro... into thrombin. This changes ...fibrinogen... into fibrin fibres.

HEART

The external features of the heart

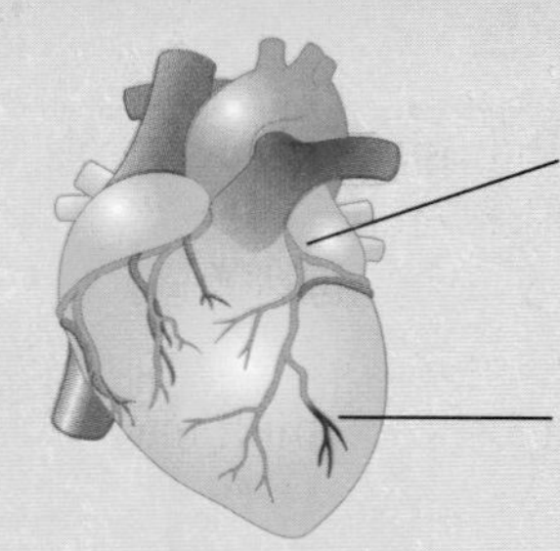

The coronary artery supplies the heart with substances such as oxygen and glucose.

The coronary vein takes substances such as carbon dioxide away from the heart.

The internal features of the heart

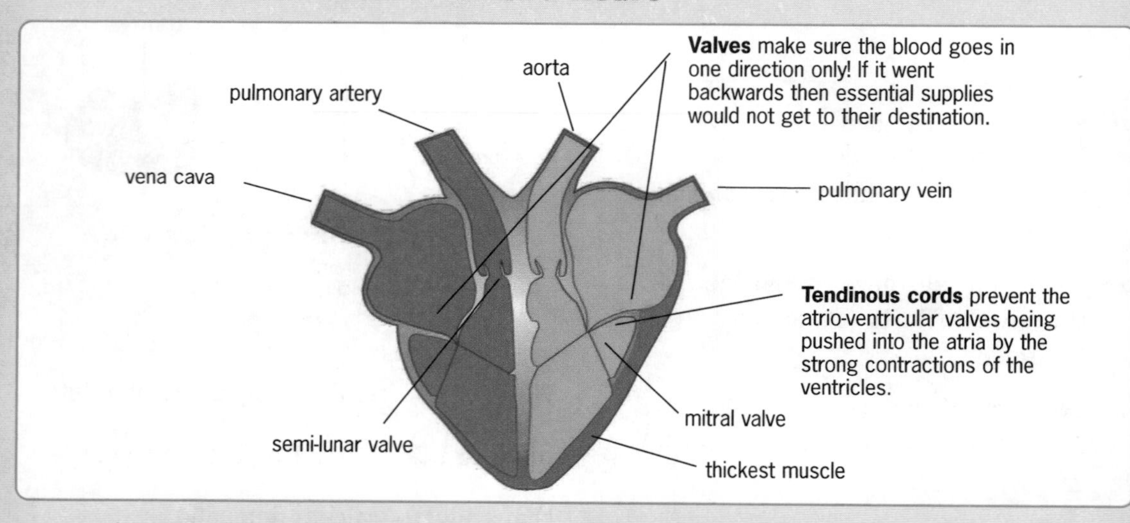

Valves make sure the blood goes in one direction only! If it went backwards then essential supplies would not get to their destination.

Tendinous cords prevent the atrio-ventricular valves being pushed into the atria by the strong contractions of the ventricles.

The heart at work!

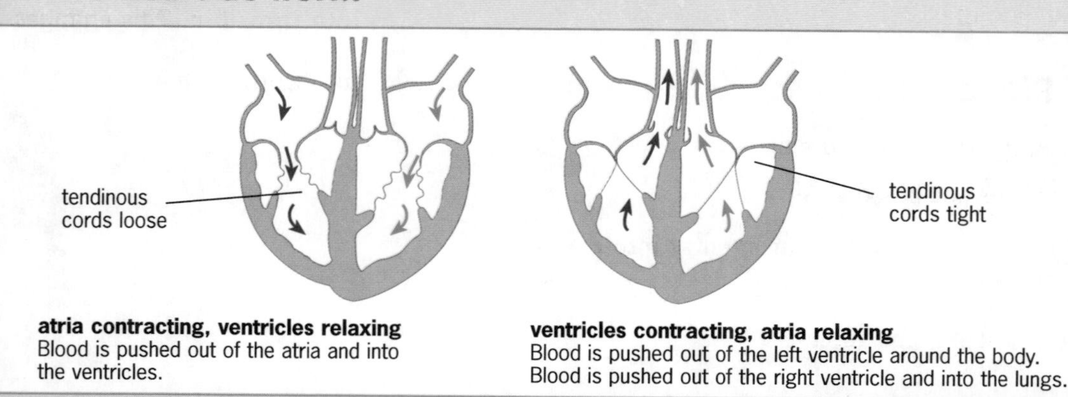

atria contracting, ventricles relaxing
Blood is pushed out of the atria and into the ventricles.

ventricles contracting, atria relaxing
Blood is pushed out of the left ventricle around the body.
Blood is pushed out of the right ventricle and into the lungs.

Cardiac muscle never tires and keeps the heart pumping for your entire life.

Atherosclerosis

Atherosclerosis is the build up of cholesterol in the blood vessels, which reduces the space available for blood. This means the efficiency of blood flow is reduced. Blood pressure increases. What do you think may happen if a total blockage prevents the supply of oxygen and glucose to the heart muscles? Yes – a heart attack!

Progress check

Blood flows from the artery, to the capillaries, then to the veins.
The different blood vessels have different pressures.

Choose which blood pressure (in arbitrary units) matches which blood vessel.

15
25
50

	Artery	Capillary	Vein
Pressure	50	25	15

RESPIRATION

Aerobic respiration releases *lots* of energy.

glucose + oxygen → carbon dioxide + water + lots of energy

Aerobic respiration takes place in cells with the help of mitochondria. We can respire aerobically, e.g. an athlete in a long-distance race uses aerobic respiration.

How is oxygen supplied to the body for aerobic respiration?

Oxygen is taken into the body through breathing in! Waste carbon dioxide and water vapour are then breathed out.

The stages of breathing in (inhalation)

Diaphragm muscles contract, so diaphragm lowers
↓
External intercostal muscles contract
↓
This contraction causes rib cage to move upwards and outwards
↓
Pressure in chest cavity becomes low
↓
This causes pressure in lungs to become low
↓
Atmospheric pressure is greater than pressure in lungs
↓
Air flows in through the nose and mouth, down the trachea and into the lungs

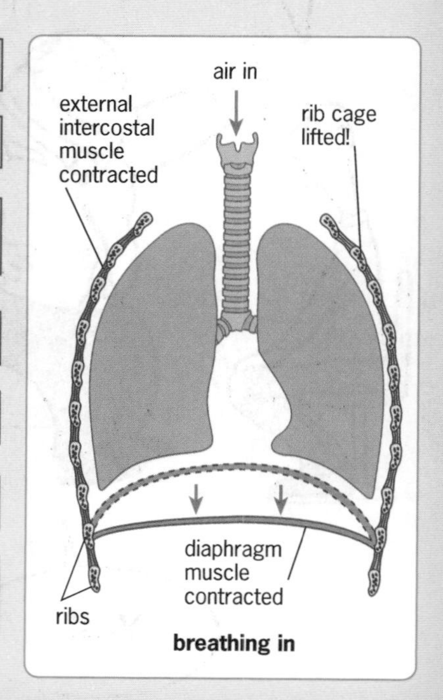

breathing in

All energy release in cells is known as respiration and it takes place in all living cells.

Anaerobic respiration releases a small amount of energy.

The reaction in plants is:

> glucose → ethanol + carbon dioxide + water + **a small amount of energy**

A dormant seed uses anaerobic respiration. Energy reserves can last a long time!

The reaction in animals is:

> glucose → lactic acid + **a small amount of energy**

Animals use anaerobic respiration in addition to aerobic respiration as a **top-up** for their energy needs. An athlete running in a 100 m sprint has a massive energy requirement so anaerobic respiration in the muscles teams up with aerobic respiration.

Anaerobic respiration produces **lactic acid**. Continuous anaerobic respiration results in an **oxygen debt** that has to be repaid. This is so that lactic acid can be broken down into carbon dioxide and water.

Progress check

1. Anaerobic respiration by yeast is used to produce alcoholic drinks. The diagrams below show how yeast ferments grape juice to make wine. Circle 'more' or 'less' for each item in the fermentation vessel.

During day 1 | After 30 days

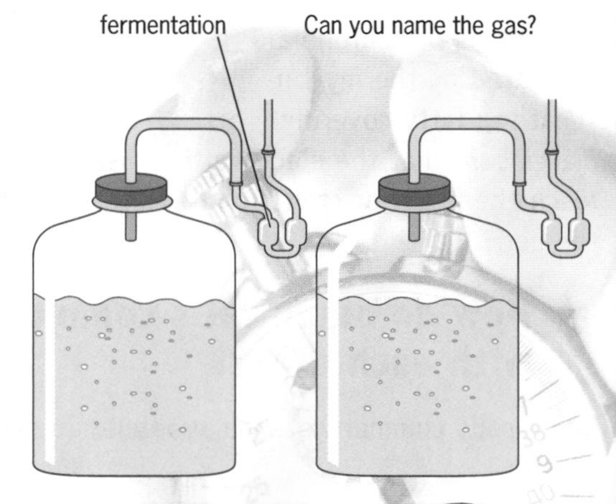

yeast	more/less
glucose	more/less
alcohol	more/less

yeast	more/less
glucose	more/less
alcohol	more/less

2. What are the stages of breathing out (exhalation).

ribs fall back in and Waste products are breathed out through nose + mouth

NERVES

What are the special features of neurones?

All neurones communicate by sending and receiving electrical impulses. Neurones are like normal cells, having a cell membrane, nucleus and cytoplasm, but each has other special features.

- **Motor neurone** – this cell controls muscular contraction.
- **Sensory neurone** – this cell responds to a stimulus such as light, sound, touch (pressure).

direction of electrical impulse
cell body
axon
myelin (fatty) sheath
When the impulse reaches the muscle, it contracts.
muscle
direction of electrical impulse
The receptor responds to the stimulus by beginning an impulse.
receptor

Both types of neurone are **insulated** by the myelin sheath, a fatty covering. This makes sure that the electrical impulses reach their destination. Sensory impulses must reach the **brain** or **spinal cord**. Motor impulses must reach the **muscles** or glands of the body.

How do nerve cells communicate with each other?

Nerve cells communicate via **synapses** (a synapse is a gap).

An **electrical impulse** arrives along an axon

↓

Transmitter molecules pass across the gap

↓

If **enough** transmitter molecules reach the next cell then an electrical impulse takes place in the next cell

↓

The transmitter substances bind to **specific proteins** on the cell membrane of the next cell

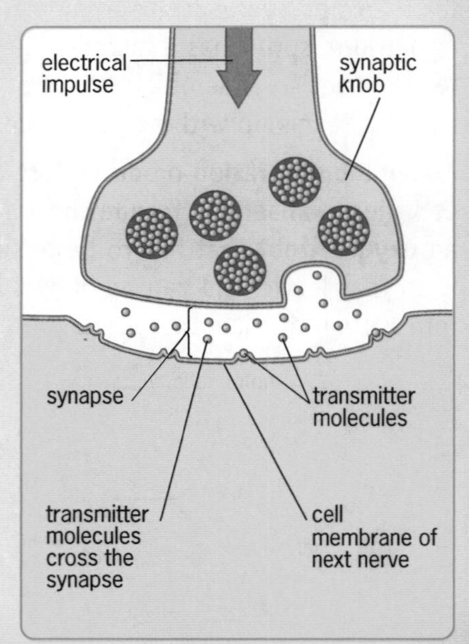

Drugs can affect synapses. They can speed up, slow down or even stop transmitter substances across a synapse.

Multipolar neurones

These cells are found in the brain and spinal cord. You have millions of them. Each interacts with others through their many synapses. They are important to your **intelligence** and **memory**. These neurones link the sensory neurones to the motor neurones.

Reflexes

You never have to stop to think about dropping a very hot plate. It just happens. The speed of reaction depends on a reflex arc. A reflex arc has the shortest route for electrical impulses to travel so it is lightning quick. This is a simple reflex arc:

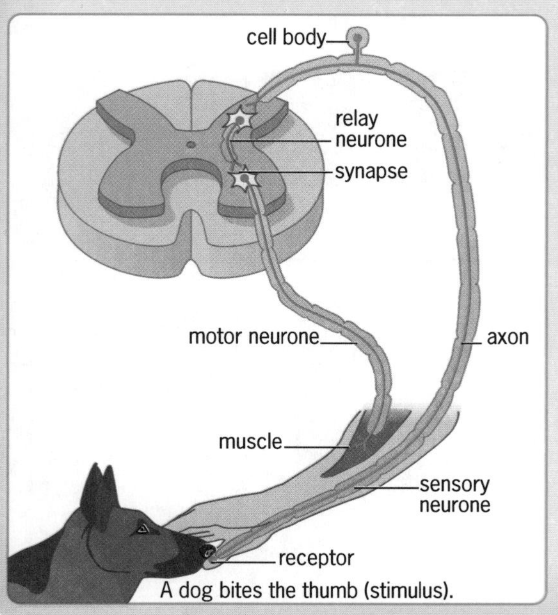

A dog bites the thumb (stimulus).

Progress check

The following are all parts of a reflex arc but they are in the wrong order. Begin with the stimulus and write them down in the correct order.

- synapse
- muscle
- motor neurone
- receptor
- dorsal root
- relay neurone
- stimulus
- synapse
- spinal cord
- sensory neurone
- axon

BRAIN

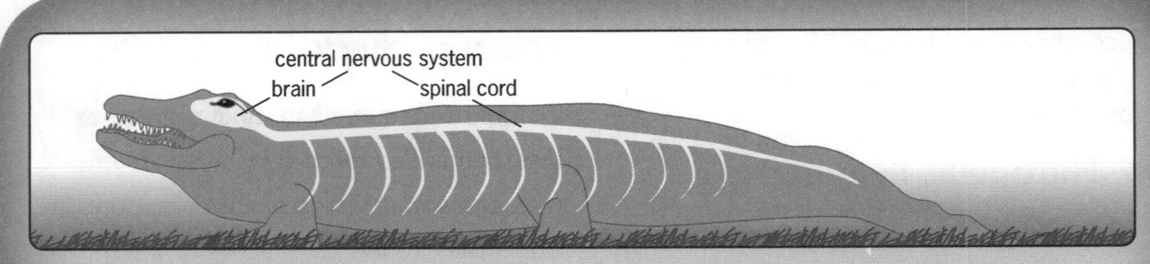

A map of the brain!

The brain does many different jobs. Here are some important ones.

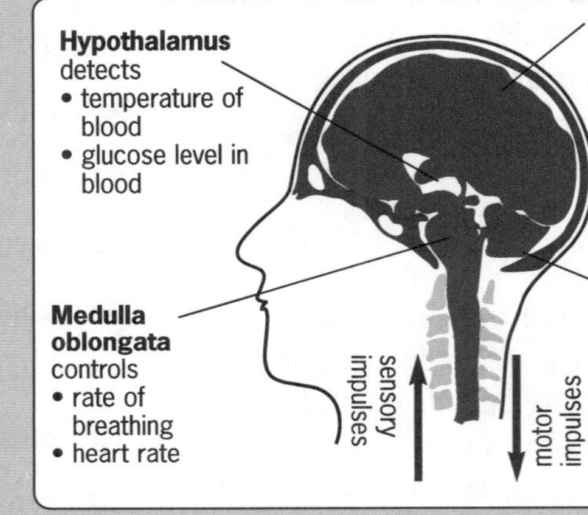

Central nervous system

The model spinal cord is like a motorway with traffic in two directions.

- Sensory impulses from other organs to the brain.
- Motor impulses from the brain to other organs.

Sometimes there is an accident, causing a break in the spinal cord. Impulses cannot pass! What would be the consequences?

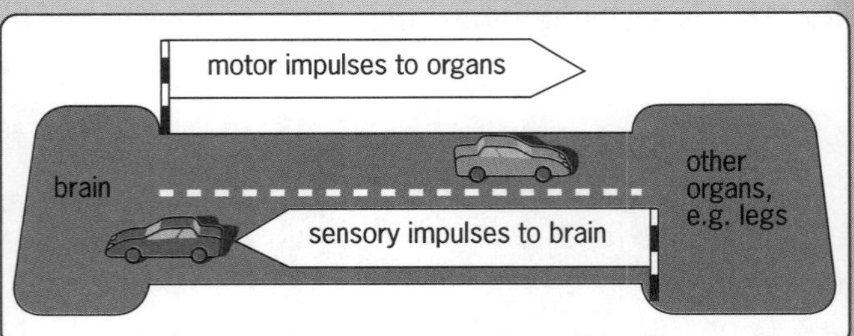

The eye

1. **cornea** — transparent, refracts light
2. **iris** — muscles, change pupil size
3. **pupil** — hole allowing light in lens
4. **lens** — transparent, refracts light, focuses light on retina
5. **suspensory ligaments** — attaches ciliary body to lens
6. **ciliary body** — changes shape of lens
7. **retina** — sensitive to light
8. **blind spot** — no light-sensitive cells here
9. **optic nerve** — takes impulses to brain

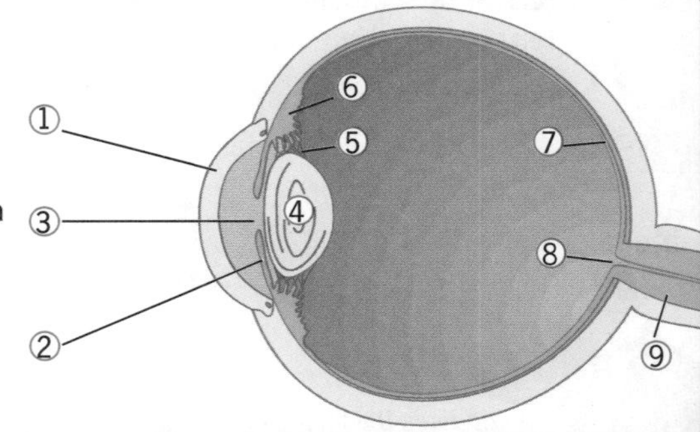

The brain and spinal cord form the central nervous system. Together they help us to receive sensory information, and respond suitably.

The human eye

The eye is sensitive to light. The image must be focused perfectly on the retina to give excellent sight. Light is focused through both the cornea and the lens.

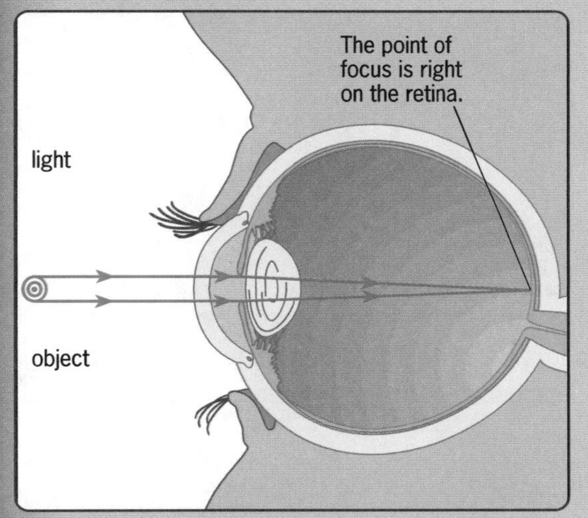

Focusing

We focus on near objects and far objects in different ways. The table shows what takes place when we focus on a near object and a far object.

	Shape of lens	Suspensory ligaments	Ciliary body
Near object	round	slack	contracted
Far object	long and thin	tight	relaxed

Progress check

For you to see, enough light must reach the retina. Too much light and the retina is damaged. When the circular muscles of the iris contract, the pupil becomes smaller, so less light enters the eye. When the radial muscles of the iris contract, the pupil becomes bigger, so more light enters the eye. **(When radial muscles are contracted, circular muscles are relaxed.)**

Complete the table to describe the state of each eye.

	A	B
radial muscle	contracted	relaxed
circular muscle	relaxed	contracted
pupil	bigger	smaller
amount of light	~~not alot~~ LOTS	Alot LITTLE

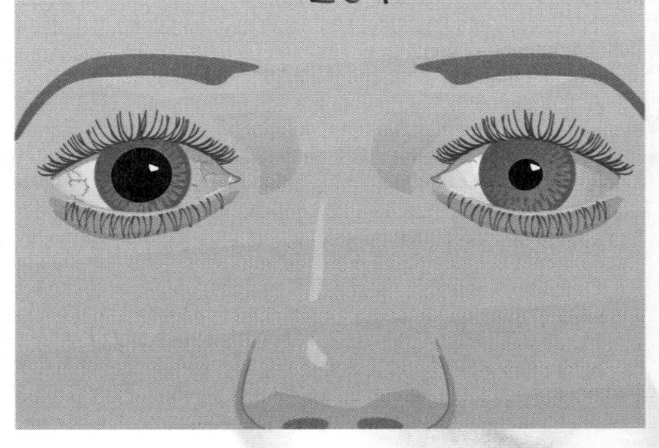

A B

HORMONES

Adrenaline – the fight or flight hormone!

Adrenaline is made during an emergency, e.g. an attack by a mugger, or before and during a race.

Effects of adrenaline

Breathing rate faster
↓
More oxygen enters blood
↓
More carbon dioxide leaves blood
↓
Heart beats faster
↓
More oxygen reaches organs, e.g. muscles
↓
More glucose released by liver into blood
↓
More energy can be released by respiration

Testosterone – the male hormone

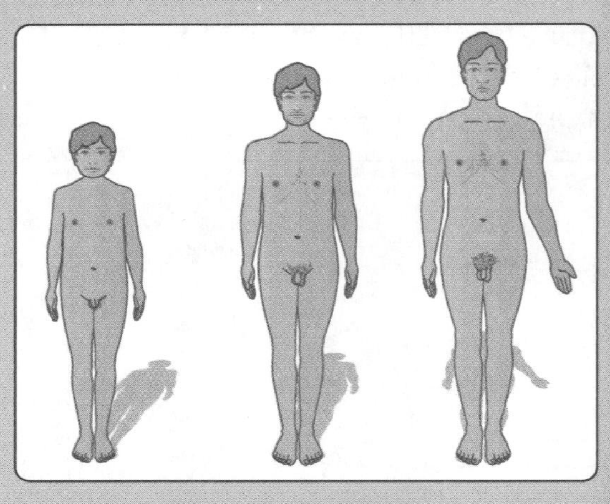

Production of testosterone increases during adolescence resulting in male characteristics.

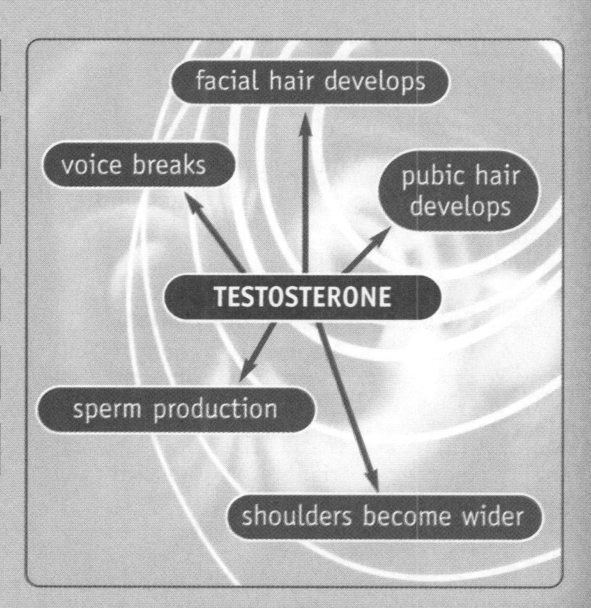

Hormones are chemical messages that are secreted by endocrine glands into the blood.

10 MINS

Oestrogen – a female hormone

Production of oestrogen increases during adolescence resulting in female characteristics.

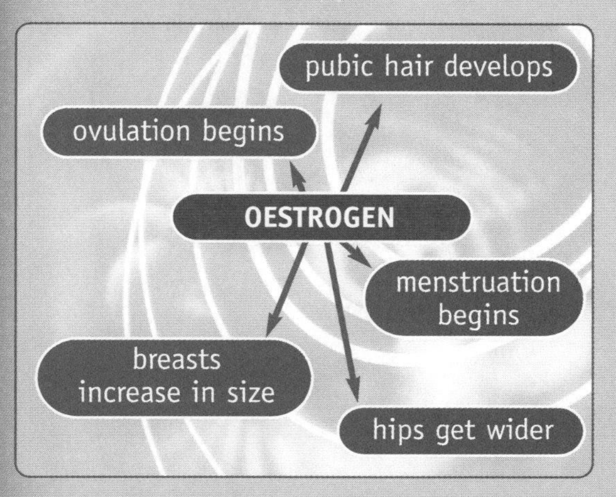

Insulin – controls glucose in blood

Insulin is produced by the pancreas after we have digested a meal containing carbohydrate. It:

- reduces glucose in blood
- allows glucose into cells for respiration
- allows excess glucose into liver

Glucose is changed to glycogen in the liver. So the liver stores glycogen, which it can change back into glucose later.

KIDNEYS

Blood rich in toxic urea enters a kidney in the renal artery. Inside the kidney, blood is filtered by the most important structure, the kidney **nephron**. Some of the urea is filtered out. Thousands of nephrons work 24 hours per day to avoid this toxic build up!

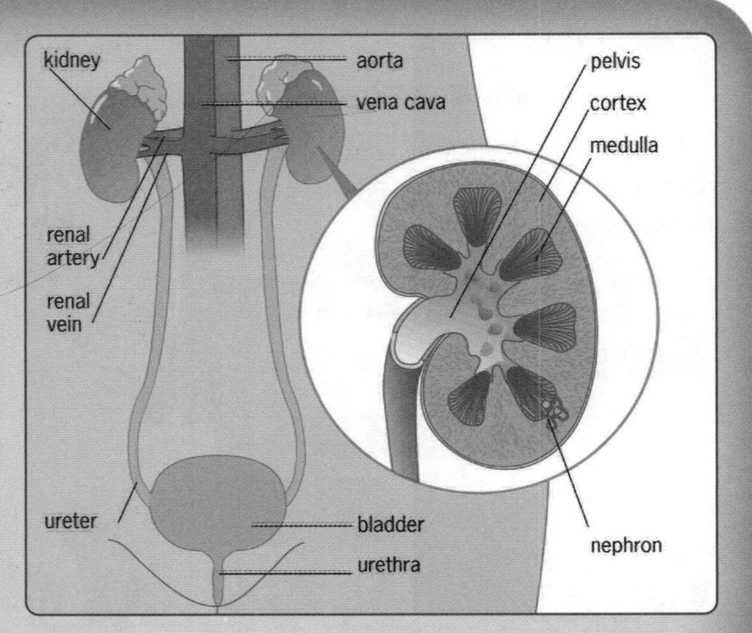

The nephron

Capillaries from the renal artery lead to the Bowman's capsule. They form a 'knot' of capillaries called the **glomerulus**.

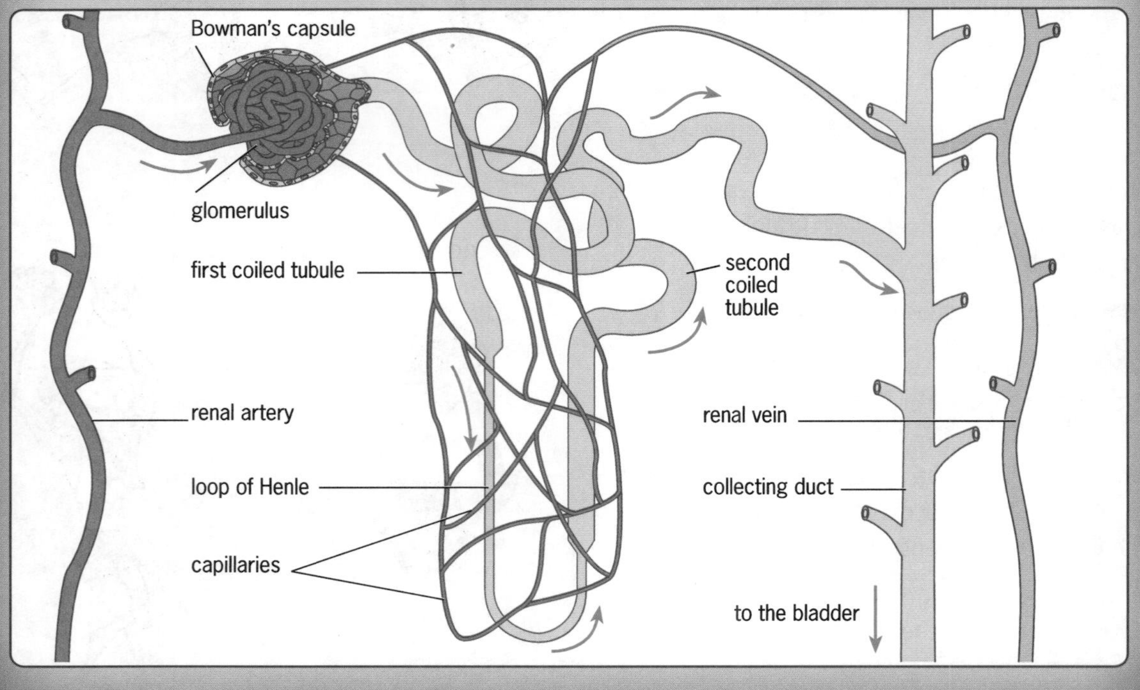

The kidneys filter the blood. Urea is made in the liver, transported in the blood to the kidneys, and passed into the bladder to be excreted in the urine.

15 MINS

DAY 2

Ultrafiltration

- Blood from renal artery arrives at a glomerulus at **high pressure**.
- There are tiny **holes** in Bowman's capsule.
- Only the smallest molecules, **water**, **urea** and **glucose**, can pass through the holes.
- Blood cells and proteins **cannot** pass through the holes (they are too big).
- The **glomerular filtrate** moves along the tubule.

Reabsorption

- Reabsorption occurs when a substance moves from a tubule, through a capillary, **back into the blood**.
- **100% of glucose** is reabsorbed at the first coiled tubule.
- **80% of water** is reabsorbed at the first coiled tubule.

What happens to the urea and the rest of the water?

No urea is reabsorbed! More water can be reabsorbed but this depends on how much water we have lost by sweating. If we sweat a lot, we reabsorb more water. If we sweat little, then we reabsorb less water.

Urea moves through the nephron, down the ureters and into the bladder. Later it can be excreted when we urinate.

Progress check

Occasionally a person may have diseased kidneys. There are two ways to help them.

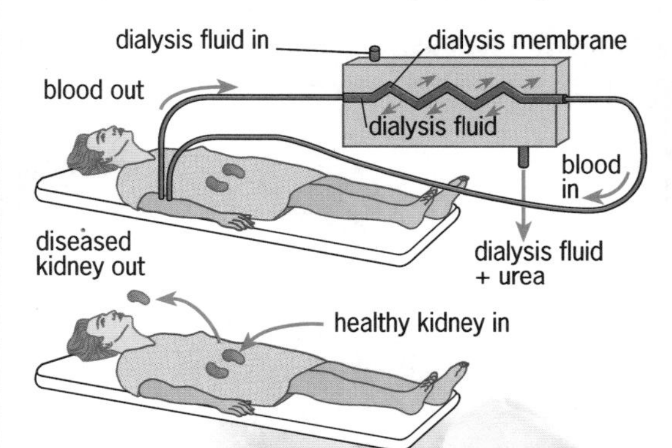

Each statement below describes the diagram above of either dialysis or transplant. For each statement indicate D for dialysis or T for transplant.

Statement	
Dialysis membrane is partially permeable	D
Filtered blood pumped back to a vein	D
Blood linked from an artery to dialysis machine	D
A donor can be living or have recently died	T
Kidney is taken from a donor	T
Kidney must be matched so that it is not rejected	T
Urea leaves blood	D

HOMEOSTASIS

Hypothalamus – the thermostat of the body!

Blood vessels close to the hypothalamus of the brain have a number of sensors, including those for temperature and water content of the blood.
The information allows adjustments to be made in either direction, up or down.
The hypothalamus, like a thermostat, can switch body systems on or off.

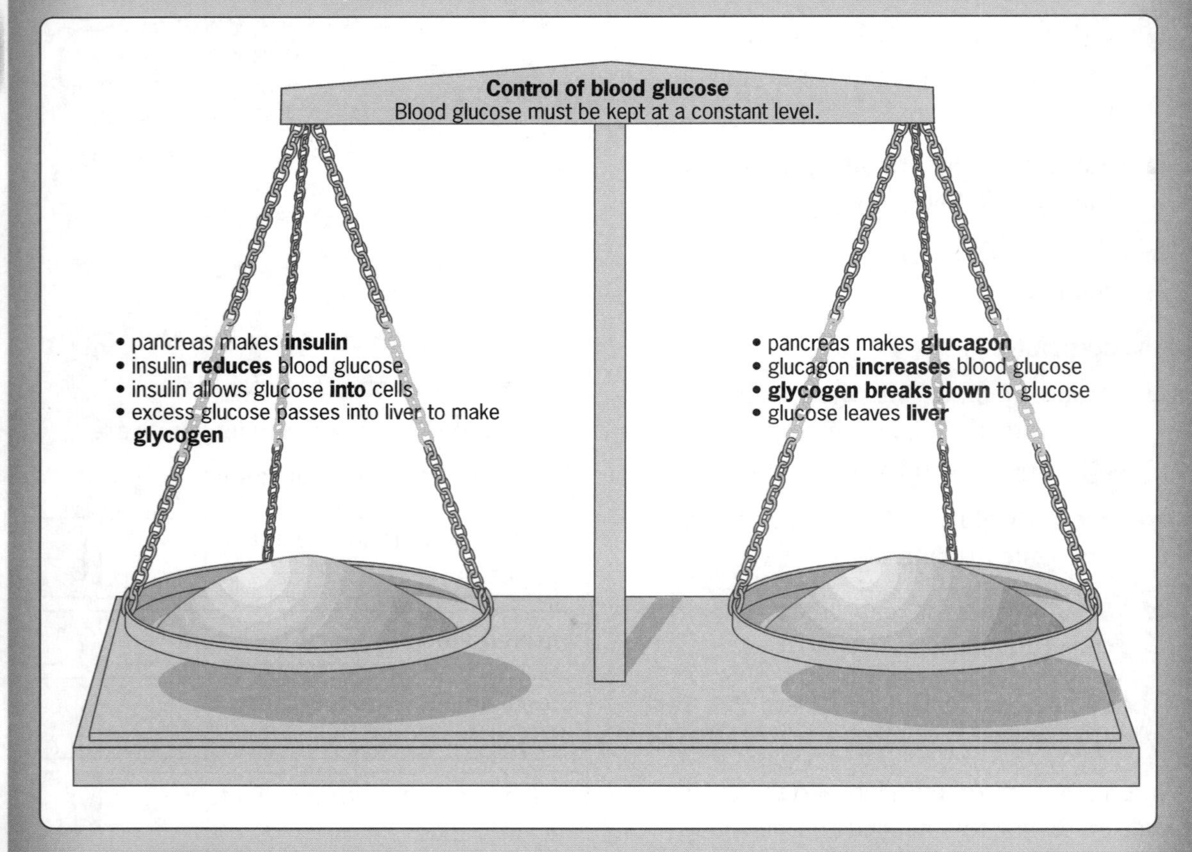

Diabetes

Diabetes that develops in young people is a condition caused by **not enough insulin** being made by the pancreas. As a result, **blood glucose cannot be regulated**. The only answer at present is to **inject insulin** each day. The amount of carbohydrate eaten must be matched to the insulin injected.

We need to have a balanced internal environment. This is homeostasis.

15 MINS

Control of body temperature

It is important that the blood temperature is kept at 37 °C. This is the optimum temperature for enzyme-controlled reactions. Higher or lower and the rate of chemical reactions does not take place correctly. We feel really ill and our lives could be in danger.

low temperature | **high temperature**

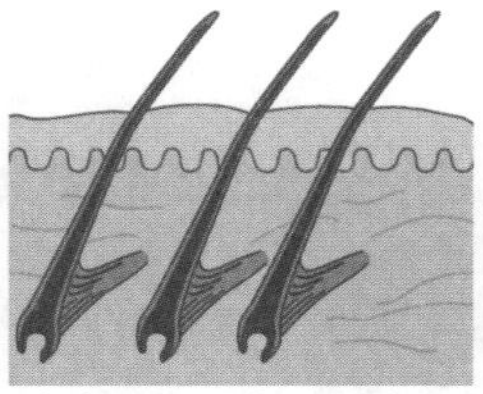

- hairs on end, trap air
- air is an insulator
- more body heat retained

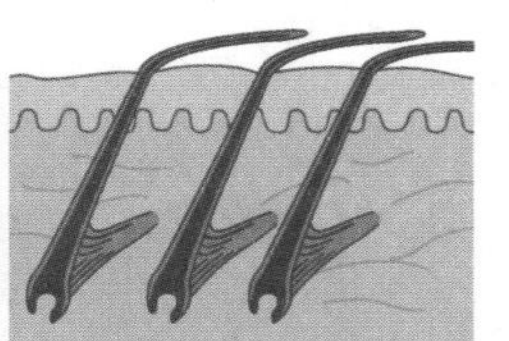

- hairs lie flat
- no air trapped
- more body heat lost

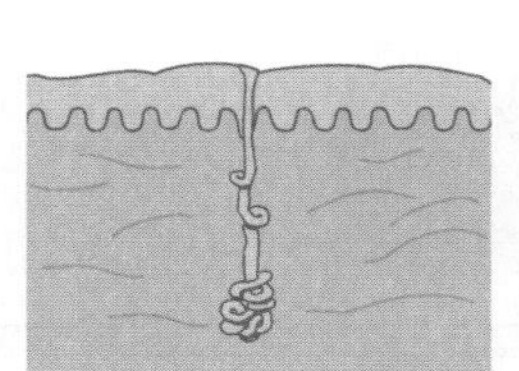

less sweating

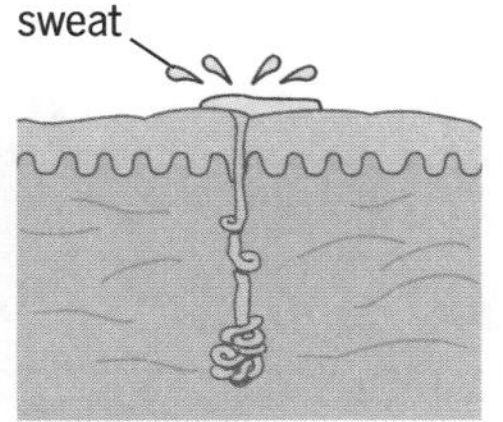

more sweating

arteriole constricted

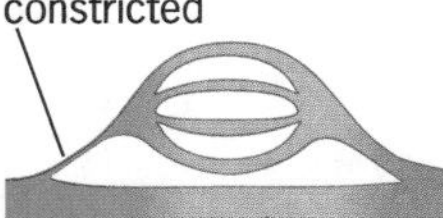

shunt vessel

blood sent to body core (vasoconstriction)

arteriole dilated

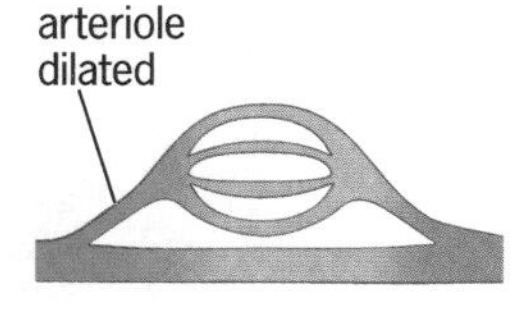

more blood to skin capillaries (vasodilation)

Progress check

The problem: too much water in the blood and blood pressure is high. Too much water lost in urine and the pressure is low.

The answer: ADH, antidiuretic hormone, is secreted by the pituitary.

The table shows what happens when there is too little water in the blood.

Complete the table to show what happens when there is too much water in the blood.

Clue: it is the opposite!

Water content in blood too low	Water content in blood too high
more ADH	less
more water reabsorbed by kidney	less...
less water in urine	more

INHERITANCE

The nucleus: the site of inheritance

We have 23 pairs of chromosomes in each nucleus. Other organisms have different numbers.

a human body cell
nucleus
chromosome

A homologous pair of chromosomes

Genes exist in different forms, known as alleles. An allele may be **dominant** or **recessive**.

We inherit one set of chromosomes from Mum and one set from Dad. Dominant genes are shown by an upper-case letter, e.g. **B**, which may stand for BROWN EYES. Recessive genes are shown as a lower-case letter, e.g. **b**, for blue eyes.

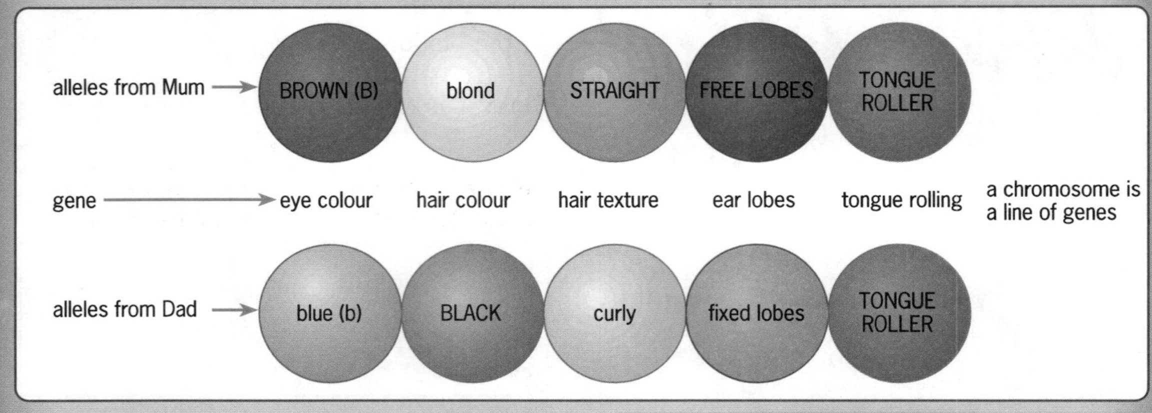

When inherited, a dominant allele is **expressed** in the offspring. A recessive allele is only expressed if the other allele is also recessive. If the two alleles are the same, it does not matter if the alleles are recessive or dominant!

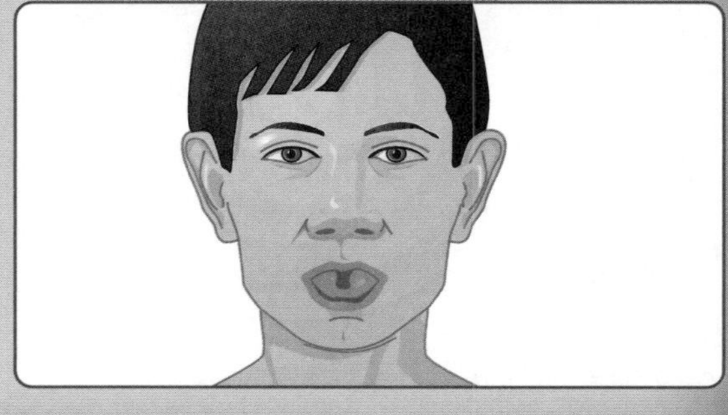

A person with the alleles above would have

- brown eyes
- straight hair
- black hair
- free lobes
- and be a tongue roller

Genes are responsible for the development of all characteristics and are passed on from parents to offspring.

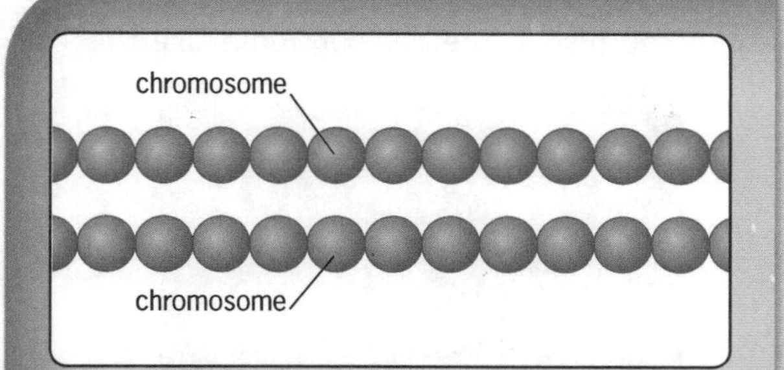

Genetics dictionary

Homozygous	Both alleles for a gene are the same, e.g. BB, bb
Heterozygous	The two alleles for a gene are different, e.g. Bb
Genotype	This includes all alleles inherited from parents, both dominant and recessive, e.g. Bb – even the alleles that are carried but not shown are included
Phenotype	This includes only the alleles that are expressed, e.g. B (the one that is actually shown in the person)
Diploid	This means that the chromosomes in a body cell are in pairs – one set comes from Mum and one from Dad, so that is 23 pairs in a body cell
Haploid	This means that there is one set of chromosomes in some cells – in humans a sperm and ovum each have a single set of 23 chromosomes

Progress check

Our alleles are B = Brown eyes and b = blue eyes.
David has the genotype bb and Ann has the genotype Bb. What are the possible genotypes of their babies? Use this genetic diagram to help you.

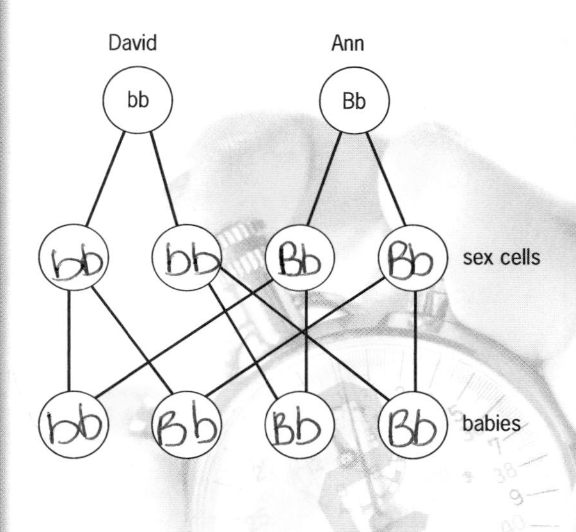

CELL DIVISION

There are two types of cell division: mitosis and meiosis. Simple organisms such as amoeba are only capable of mitosis but we can do both.

A cell just before division looks like this:

Mitosis – a cell divides to form two identical cells.

1 prophase

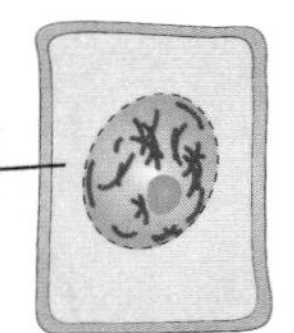

2 metaphase

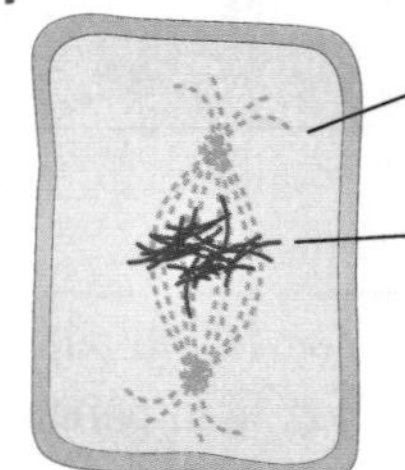

3 anaphase

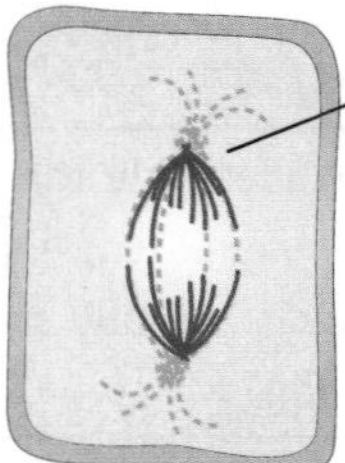

4 telophase

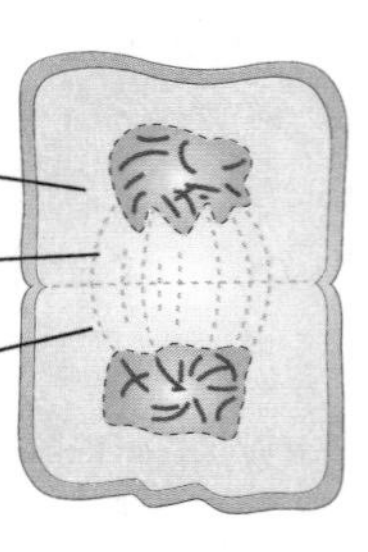

What are the differences between mitosis and meiosis?

	Mitosis	Meiosis
How many daughter cells are produced?	2	4
Are the daughter cells identical?	Yes	No – every one is different!
How many sets of chromosomes are there?	2	1
Are the chromosomes single or in pairs?	single	pairs

New cells are needed for reproduction, growth and repair. This supply is created by cell division.

Where do mitosis and meiosis take place in the human body?

All **growth** and **repair** of cells take place through mitosis. Meiosis is important for the reproduction of our species. Our body cells contain 46 chromosomes. Imagine what would happen if sperms and ova each had 46. When they fused at fertilisation there would be 92 chromosomes. These cells would die because they had too many chromosomes!

Meiosis makes sex cells (gametes), each having 23 chromosomes – a **haploid** number. When the sperm and ovum fuse then the cell becomes **diploid** as the number of 46 chromosomes is regained.

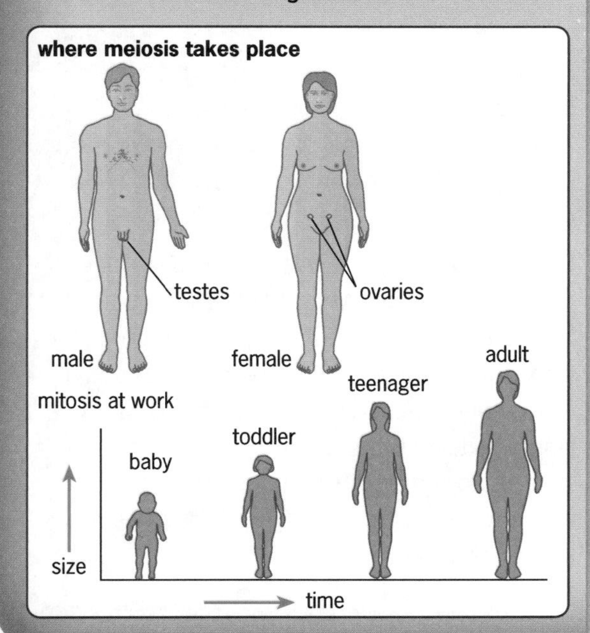

Progress check

The diagram shows one stage in the process of mitosis.

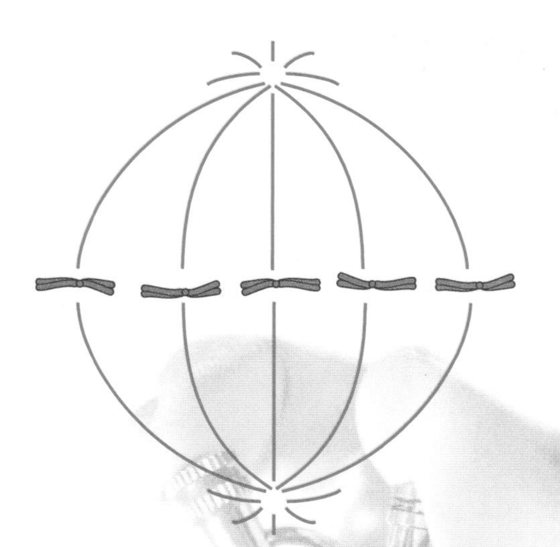

1. Name the stage of mitosis. Give a reason for your answer.

   telophase because the centromeres split

2. How many chromosomes would the parent cell have had?

   12B.

(1) metaphase

(2) 5

SEXUAL REPRODUCTION

10 MINS

DAY 2

What makes the sex cells?

The sex cells are called **gametes**. The male gamete is the **sperm**, and the female gamete is the **ovum**. When we get close to our adult stage, the reproductive systems supply mature eggs and sperms ready for fertilisation.

Male reproductive system

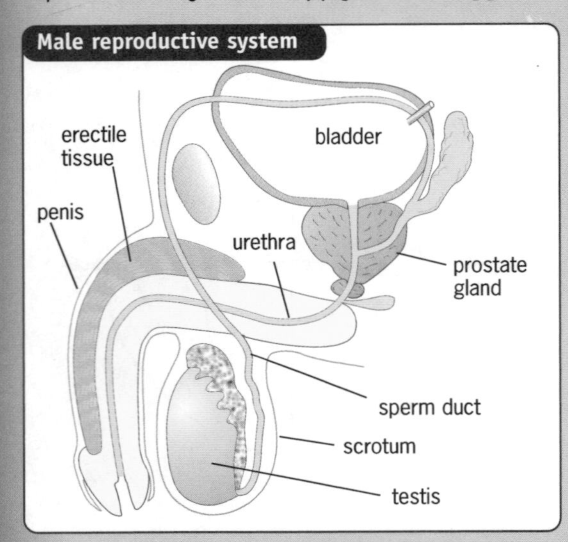

Female reproductive system

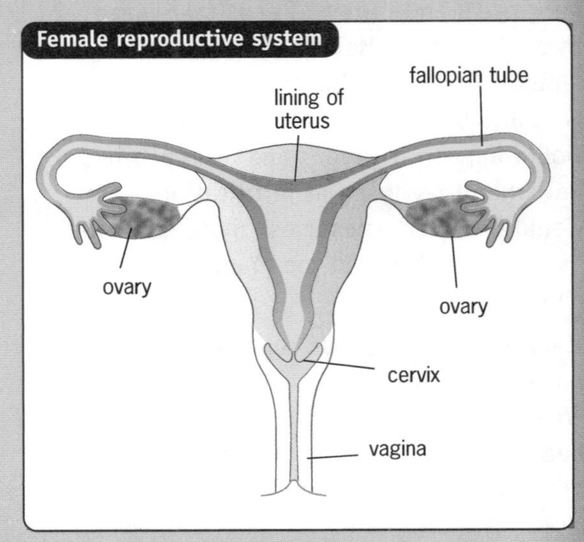

Sperm and eggs: the full story!

Sperms are made by the **testes**. They can be stored for a while until sexual excitement takes place. Blood flows into the **erectile tissue**, making the penis hard instead of the normal soft condition. While hard, the penis can be put into the vagina. Stimulation in this situation results in ejaculation. Millions of sperms are released from the testes and pass through the **sperm duct**. Fluid is added by glands, e.g. prostate, along the way. The sperms plus fluid are known as **semen**. The fluid allows the sperms to swim and gives nutrients. The flow of semen is one way. Once released, sperms flow like a tidal wave along the sperm duct, through the **urethra** and out of the penis.

Ova are made by the **ovaries**. Usually one ovum is produced per month. The ovum leaves the ovary and begins a journey down a **fallopian tube**. If no sperm cell enters the female, then the journey ends as this tiny egg leaves the body via the vagina. If sperms do reach the fallopian tube and an ovum is on its journey, then fertilisation may take place.

Some organisms need males and females for sexual reproduction to continue the species.

Fertilisation at work

The head of the first sperm that reaches the ovum enters it through the cell membrane. The two nuclei fuse together as the sperm tail falls away. A male produces millions of sperms but only one is needed for fertilisation.

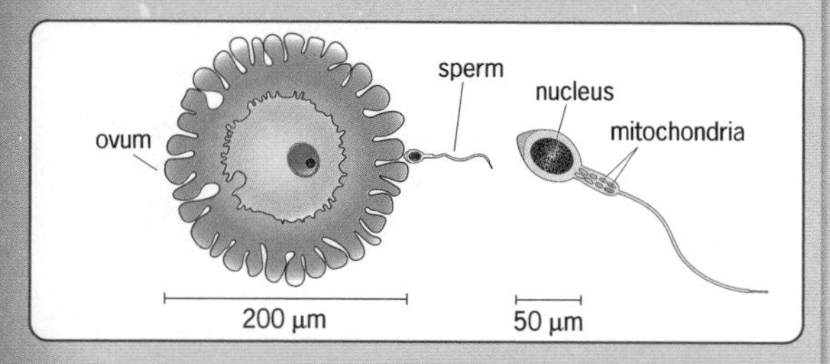

The story of implantation

Once an ovum has been fertilised, it immediately starts to divide by mitosis. First it divides into 2 ... then 4 ... then 8 ... then 16 ... and so on!

A ball of cells known as an **embryo** is formed. This then undergoes **implantation** as it sticks to the lining of the uterus. The lining is full of blood capillaries and can supply the nutrients needed for the development of the **foetus**.

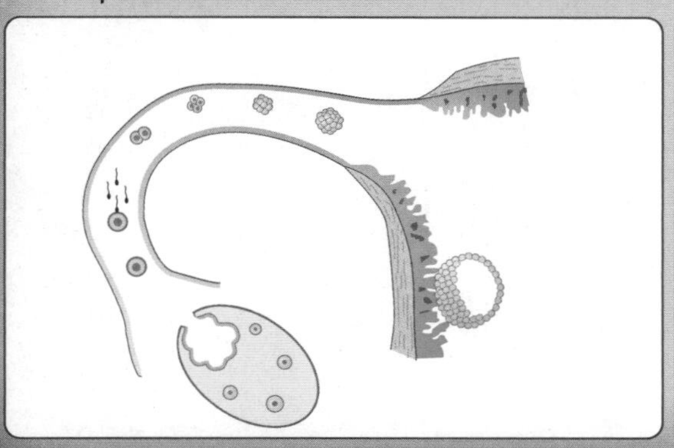

Progress check

1. Beginning with the production of a sperm in a testis and ending with the site of fertilisation in a woman, list all parts of the journey.

2. The diagram shows the formation of twins. Are the twins identical or non-identical? Give a reason for your answer.

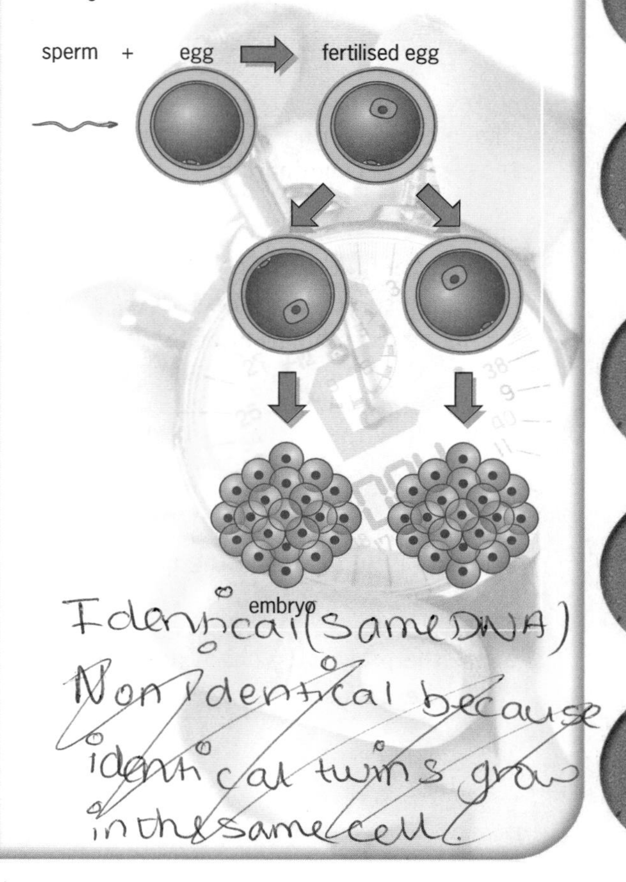

Identical (same DNA)
Non identical because identical twins grow in the same cell.

SELECTIVE BREEDING

Principle of selective breeding

Choose two parents each with a desired feature

↓

Enable them to mate

↓

Collect the offspring

↓

Test the offspring to detect if they have the new combination of desired features

↓

Keep the offspring with the desired combination

↓

Grow successful offspring to maturity; allow them to go on to breed to pass on this new combination of features

↓

Do not allow the unsuccessful offspring to breed

↓

You have now improved the gene pool

↓

Repeat the process by choosing only the best organisms to breed

Read this article from the *Poultry News*.

Sex crisis for turkeys!

Reporters have uncovered the secret behind modern turkey production. Customers prefer breast meat, so for years breeders have selected only birds with the biggest breasts to breed with. This has been very successful! Turkeys with giant breasts are now farmed.

So what is the problem? No male turkey can mate **naturally** with a female. They just cannot connect because the enormous breast structure gets in the way.

So, how do they breed? People collect semen from the male artificially. Semen is then inserted into the female by **artificial insemination**, using a catheter.

Is this moral? Is this ethical? Have the scientists ruined the life of the turkey? Turkeys certainly think so!

Selective breeding, or artificial selection, aims to produce improved plants and animals.

What has selective breeding done for us?

Selective breeding of wheat: 1930–2004

Variety	Year	Height in cm	Yield in tonnes
Grandier	1930	97.5	1.5
Centrus I	1951	86.5	2.6
Centrus II	1964	74.0	3.4
Supertop	1985	62.5	4.2
Dwarfex	2000	35.5	5.5

The stems of wheat supply straw, which is not valuable. Grain is extremely valuable. More grain means more food for people.

Use the table to work out **two** trends from 1930 to 2000. How is modern wheat better adapted to windy conditions?

Progress check

1. Give the alternative term for selective breeding.

   Artificial insemination.

2. Does selective breeding produce new genetic features? Give a reason for your answer. Yes, it can produce the gentic you want.

3. How are the parents chosen in the process of selective breeding?

   The best ones, e.g biggest

4. After selective breeding, what happens to offspring that do not have suitable features?

   Not used for breeding

5. A pupil stated that selective breeding is always successful. Is this true or false? Give a reason for your choice.

   False, the genetics do not always match, not always the dominant allele is shown.

EVOLUTION

What is the evidence for evolution? It is fossils: preserved imprints of dead organisms!

Can new genes appear?

Yes! A new gene, or a new allele can appear by **mutation**, a change in DNA. So a new characteristic can appear or an existing one can disappear. Without mutations there could be no new species. Mutations occur randomly, and may result in changes in organisms. If these changes give the organism an advantage over others, then they may be passed on to the organism's offspring. As these offspring breed, the mutation will be passed on and will spread through the community of organisms as a result. In this way, a species can change over time.

original DNA
A T T G C C T A G C C G
T A A C G G A T C G G C
and now it mutates...
A T T G C C T A G C C G A T C
T A A C G G A T C G G C T A G
Can you find the change?

What causes mutations?

- **Ionising radiation** is given off by radioactive substances.
- **Mutagenic chemicals.**

Both can change an organism's DNA.

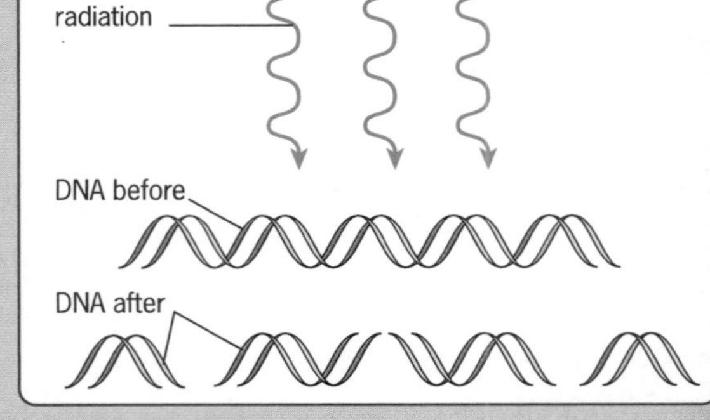

Is variation important?

Variation **within a species** is important if evolution is to take place. Each gene in a species may have a range of different alleles, e.g. a species of wild cat may have black, dark brown, light brown, white fur. One colour may give better camouflage than others so those cats may get more food.

Charles Darwin and the theory of natural selection

Darwin suggested the theory of natural selection in 1858. Over millions of years of the Earth's existence there have been changes in the weather patterns. These have ranged from very cold (Ice Age) to very warm. Some organisms are better suited than others whenever a change takes place.

The process of natural selection

The environment changes

↓

Some organisms are better adapted, so survive – these are **selected for**

↓

Other organisms are not well adapted, and are **selected against**. This means they die out, and can lead to a species becoming extinct

↓

The survivors go on to breed and pass on the advantage to their offspring

The process continues each time there is a major environmental change.

POLLUTION

Air pollution

	Amount in pollution-free air
nitrogen	78.0%
oxygen	21.0%
carbon dioxide	0.03%
water vapour	approx 0.47%
rare gases	approx 0.5%

Common air pollutants are:

- sulphur dioxide
- carbon monoxide
- nitrogen oxides
- chlorofluorocarbons (CFCs)
- methane

Example

Acid rain

Which air pollutant is guilty of the environmental crime of **acid rain**? It is **sulphur dioxide**. Every time we burn a **fossil fuel**, sulphur dioxide is given off into the air. It diffuses in the air, mixes with the **water molecules** of clouds and forms **sulphurous acid**.

When it rains, the acid in the rain destroys plants and animals. It even acidifies lakes. Herbivores lose their food source. Once they die, the carnivores are in trouble. Complete food chains can be destroyed.

Any added pollutants change the pure air percentages.

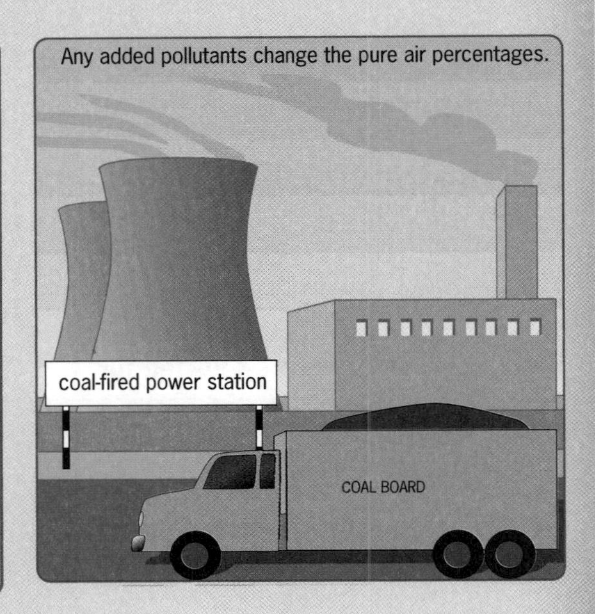

Water pollution

Some important water pollutants are:

- **oil**
- **herbicide (weedkiller)**
- **pesticides**
- **fertiliser (nitrates and phosphates)**
- **heavy metal ions**
- **sewage**

Pollution happens when a factor causes a change in the environment.

Example

Pesticides are used to kill pests on farms. Sprays 'drift' in the breeze and additionally, when it rains, **run-off** reaches rivers. Most pesticides are non-persistent as they degrade quickly in the environment. **DDT** is persistent and remains in soil, unchanged, as well as in animals' tissues. DDT was banned over 30 years ago in the UK, but it is still used in some areas of the world. In the UK kestrels almost died out because of this persistent pesticide. Eggshells were so weak that many broke.

DDT increases in concentration along the food chain – the top predator is in danger! A large fish may eat many small fish per day, hence the toxin builds up.

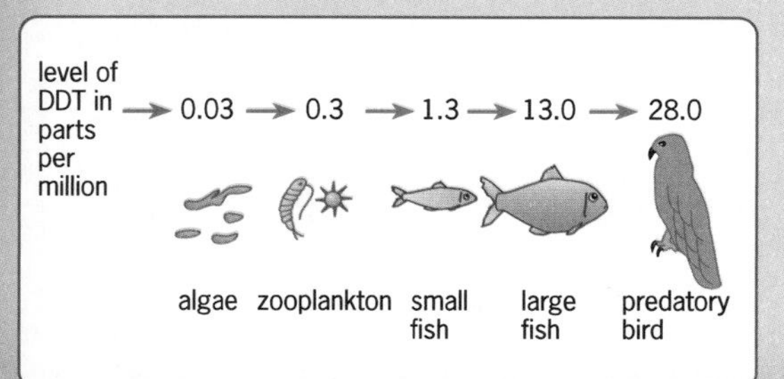

Progress check

Analyse the two graphs below. Graph 1 shows the number of people who died in one area over two weeks in 1952. Graph 2 shows the sulphur dioxide levels over the same period.

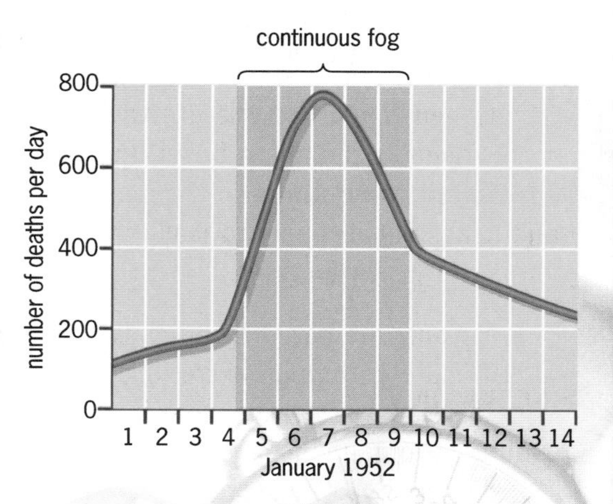

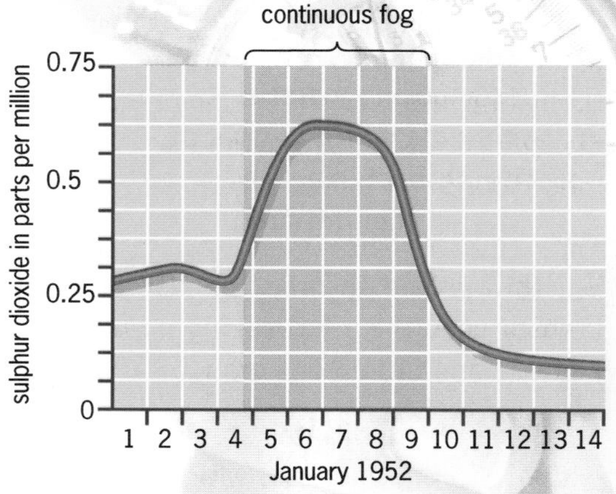

Use evidence from the graphs to suggest the cause of the deaths.

NITROGEN AND CARBON CYCLES

Nitrogen cycle: the key roles of bacteria

The air contains 79% nitrogen gas. The element nitrogen is a vital component of all proteins and DNA. We breathe in 79% and the same proportion is breathed out.

The main features of the nitrogen cycle are:

Nitrogen gas is used by **nitrogen-fixing bacteria**, many of which live in the root nodules of plants in the pea and bean family.

Nitrogen-fixing bacteria use the nitrogen in the air to **build up nitrogen compounds** so the peas and beans get a supply to make their own proteins.

The plants are eaten by animals. Ultimately, through excretion, defecation and death, there is a source of organic material which is **decomposed** by saprophytic micro-organisms.

Decomposing material gives off **ammonia** which is used by the **nitrifying bacteria** to make nitrites, then nitrates.

Nitrates are absorbed by plants, which need them for making proteins and ultimately, growth.

Some of the nitrates are used by **denitrifying bacteria**, which return the nitrogen to the atmosphere. The cycle is complete!

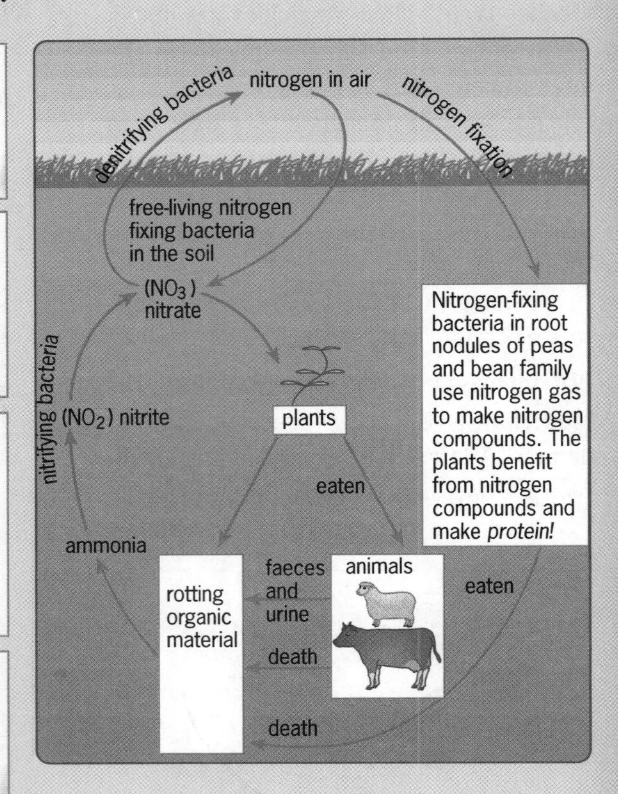

Carbon cycle: the photosynthesis–respiration 'merry-go-round'

The carbon cycle relies on both plants and animals. The atmosphere is a vast resource of carbon dioxide. Air contains 0.03% carbon dioxide.

The main features of the carbon cycle are:

Green plants use carbon dioxide in **photosynthesis** to make glucose.

Glucose is used in **respiration** to release energy for living processes.

Carbon dioxide is released during respiration and is returned to the atmosphere.

Plants are sometimes burned as a source for heat energy, either as renewable timber or as the fossil fuel coal. This releases carbon dioxide back to the air.

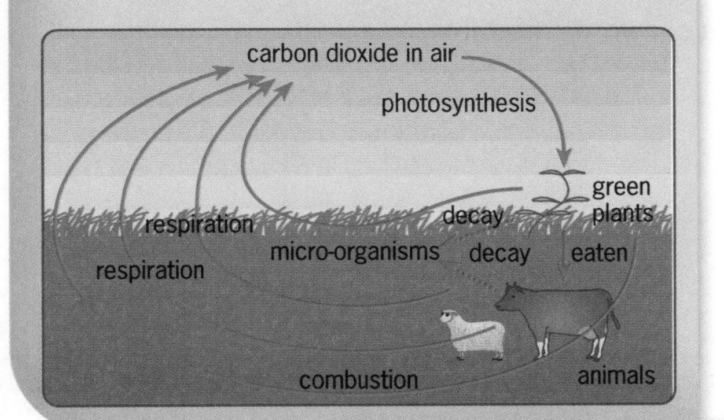

Progress check

The flow diagram shows the changes that take place as a pile of leaves decays. What would happen if bacteria X died?

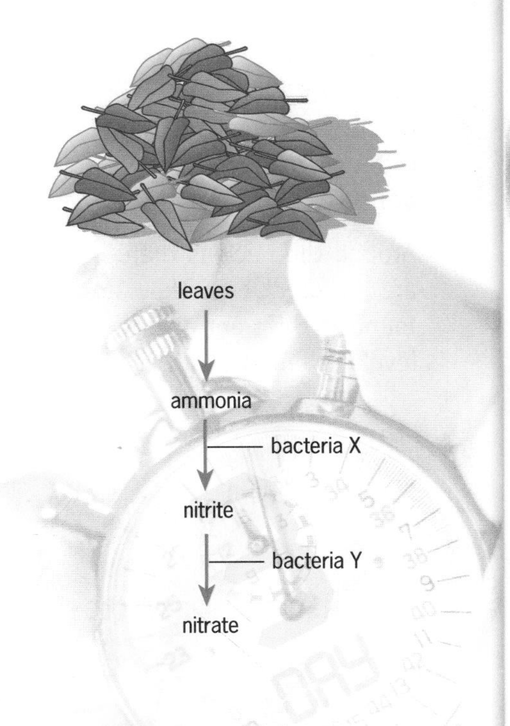

ATOMIC STRUCTURE

All substances are made up of atoms.
There are over 100 different types of atom.

Structure of an atom

- The centre of an atom is called the **nucleus**. It contains particles called **protons** and **neutrons**.
- All atoms of a particular element have the same number of protons. Atoms of different elements have different numbers of protons.
- Around the nucleus there are the **electrons**. They are found in different energy levels called **shells**.

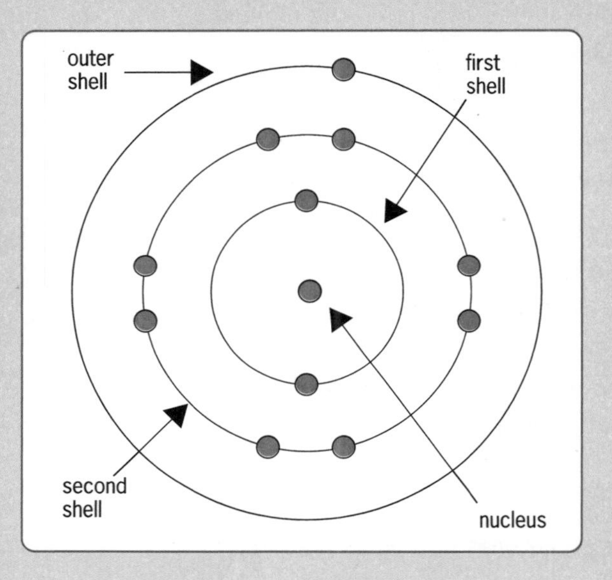

Sub-atomic particles

Protons, neutrons and electrons are collectively known as sub-atomic particles. Their mass and charge are shown in the table.

Particle	Relative mass	Charge
Proton	1	+1
Neutron	1	0
Electron	Negligible	–1

Atoms are the smallest parts of matter. An element is a substance that is made up of atoms with the same numbers of protons and electrons. However, the number of neutrons in an atom can vary.

Atomic number and mass number

The **atomic number** (or proton number) of an atom is the number of protons in an atom. In an atom, the number of protons is equal to the number of electrons, hence atoms have no overall charge. If the number of protons does not equal the number of electrons then the particle is called an **ion**.

The total number of protons and neutrons in an atom is called its **mass number**.

Representing mass number and atomic number

The mass number and atomic number of an element can be represented as follows.

mass number → $^{23}_{11}Na$ ← symbol

atomic number →

The **atomic number** of sodium is **11**. The **mass number** of sodium is **23**.

Number of protons in an atom of sodium is **11** (the atomic number of sodium is 11).

Number of electrons in an atom of sodium is **11** (the number of electrons in an atom is always the same as the number of protons).

Number of neutrons in a atom of sodium is **12** (the number of neutrons is the difference between mass number and atomic number).

Progress check

1. Which two particles make up the nucleus of an atom?
   a) protons and electrons
   b) protons and neutrons
   c) neutrons and electrons

2. What is the mass of an electron compared to the mass of a proton?

3. What is the charge on a proton?

4. Label the diagram below, showing which number is the atomic number and which is the mass number.

   $^{63}_{29}Cu$

5. Another atom of copper contains 36 neutrons. Show the mass number, atomic number and symbol for this isotope of copper in the same representation as used in question 4.

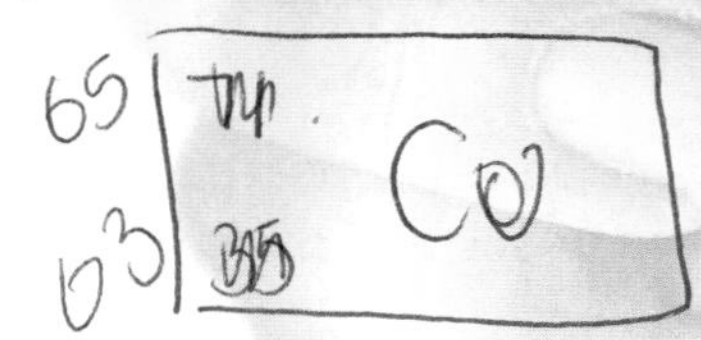

IONIC BONDING, IONIC STRUCTURES AND METALLIC BONDING

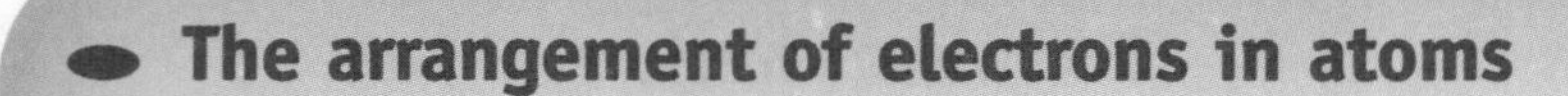

The arrangement of electrons in atoms

Electrons occupy particular energy levels (called shells) in an atom.

Electrons will fill up the lowest (innermost) energy level first.

- The first shell (i.e. the one closest to the nucleus) can hold up to two electrons.
- The outer shells can hold up to eight electrons.

You need to be able to write and draw the electron configurations for the first 20 elements only.

For example: phosphorus (atomic number 15) is 2,8,5.

The electron configuration for sodium (atomic number = 11) can be represented as shown in the diagram.

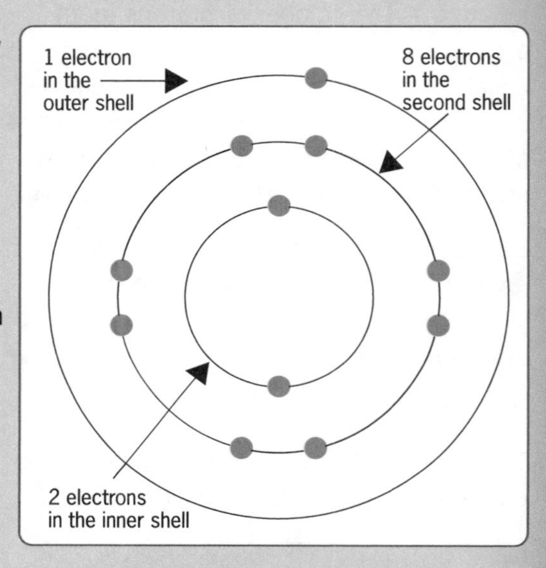

Charged atoms are called ions.

Dot-and-cross diagrams

This is a dot-and-cross diagram showing the ionic bond formation in sodium chloride.

- After the electron has been transferred from the sodium to the chlorine the atoms are charged.
- The ionic bond is the attraction between oppositely charged ions.

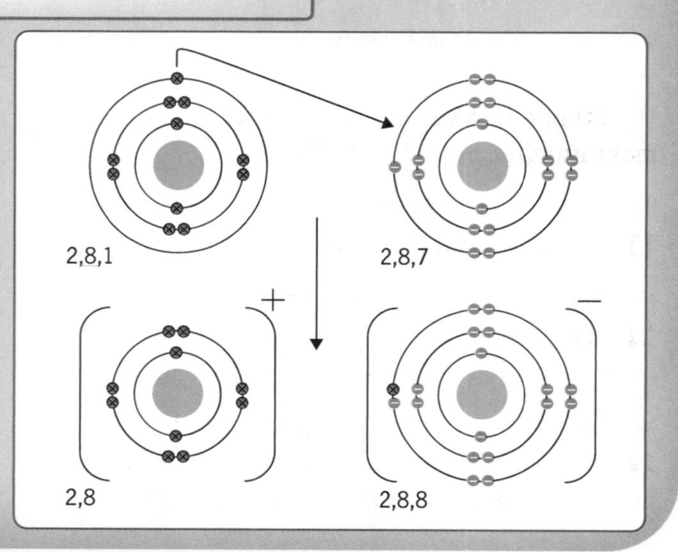

Ionic bonds occur between metals and non-metals. Electrons are transferred from metal atoms to non-metal atoms. Both atoms end up with a full outer shell of electrons.

Properties of ionic compounds

Ionic compounds form giant structures.

Ionic compounds have the following properties.

Property	Explanation
High melting and boiling points	Lots of strong bonds
Soluble in water	Water molecules are able to break down the ionic structure
Conduct electricity when molten or aqueous (dissolved in water) but not when solid	Ions need to be free moving in order for electricity to flow Mobile ions act as charge carriers

Metal structures

Metals consist of giant structures in which the electrons from the highest occupied (outer) energy levels (shells) of metal atoms are free to move through the whole structure. These free electrons:

- hold the atoms together in a regular structure
- allow the atoms to slide over each other
- allow the metal to conduct heat and electricity

The metallic bonding in sodium

Sodium atoms, for example, have one electron in their outer shell.

In a piece of metallic sodium the sodium atoms will lose this outer electron to form sodium **cations** (Na^+). The cations are arranged in a regular arrangement called a **lattice**.

The electrons move freely between these cations in what is commonly referred to as a **sea of electrons**.

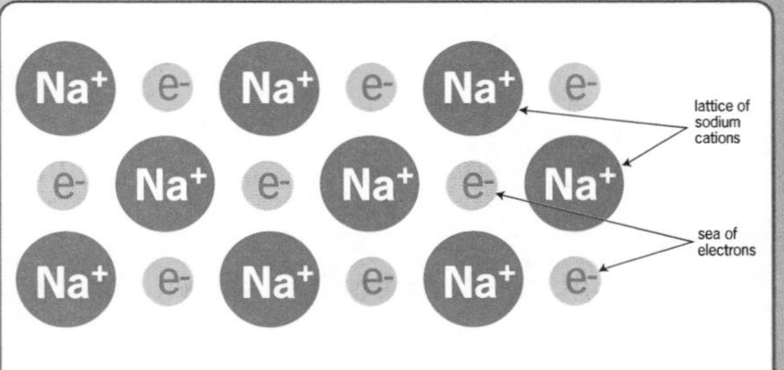

The actual bond is the attraction that exists between the metal cation and the free electrons.

COVALENT BONDING AND STRUCTURES

Covalent bond formation

The atoms in molecules are held together because they share pairs of electrons. These strong bonds between atoms are called **covalent bonds**. Like ionic bonding, covalent bonding results in the atoms ending up with a **full outer shell of electrons**.

Again, you can use a dot-and-cross diagram to show the covalent bonds in molecules.

Example 1: hydrogen chloride (HCl)

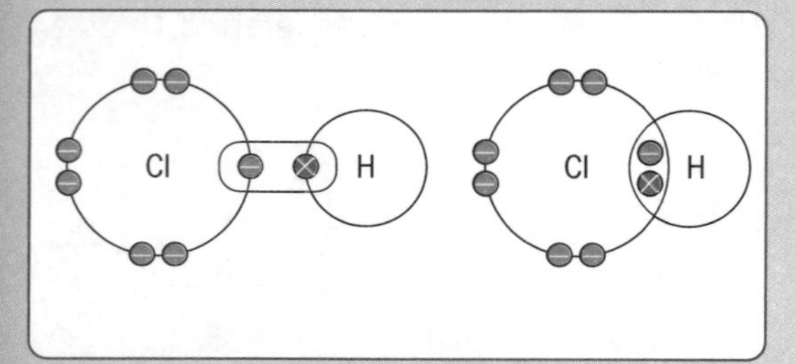

The resultant covalent bond is shown simply as a line between the two atoms.

Example 2: methane (CH_4)

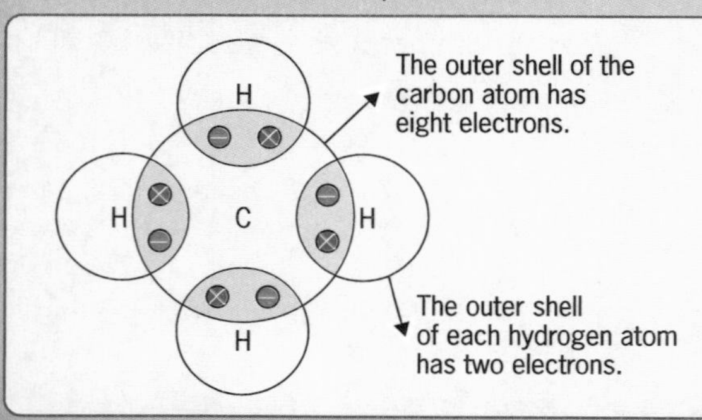

Simple covalent structures

Simple covalent structures are usually either gases (e.g. methane) or liquids (e.g. water). Properties of simple covalent compounds are shown in the table.

Property	Explanation
Relatively low melting and boiling point	Forces between molecules (intermolecular forces) are weak
Do not conduct electricity	The molecules do not carry an overall electric charge

Giant covalent structures

Diamond and graphite are good examples of giant covalent structures.

Both diamond and graphite have lots of strong covalent bonds in their structures. This is why diamond and graphite have very high melting points.

Covalent bonds are formed between two non-metal atoms. The bonds involve the sharing of electrons. There are two types of covalent structure.

In graphite, each carbon atom forms three covalent bonds and the carbon atoms form layers which are free to slide over each other. In graphite there are free electrons on the carbon atoms. This is why graphite can conduct electricity.

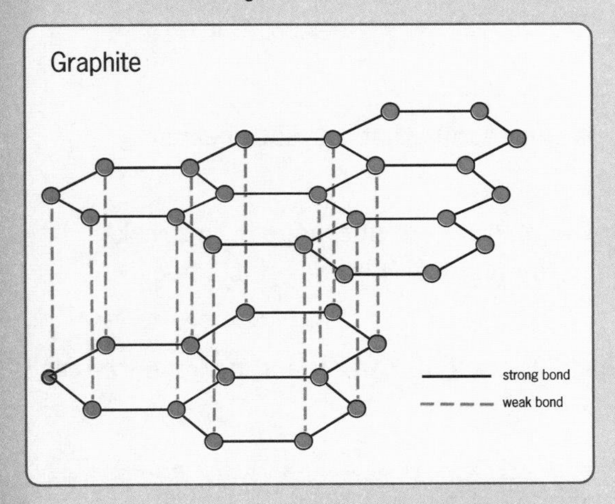

In diamond, each carbon atom forms four covalent bonds in a rigid, giant covalent structure.

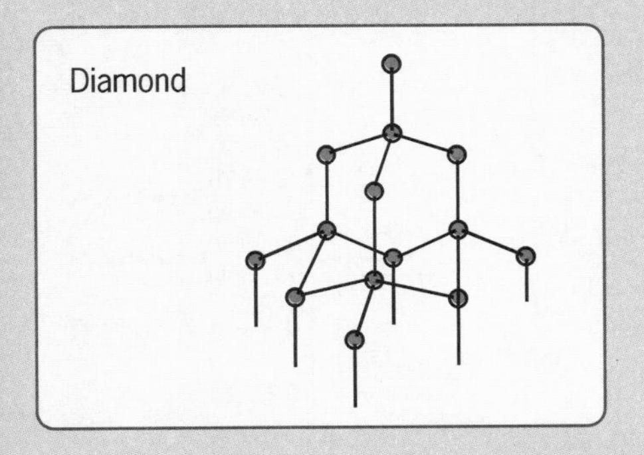

Progress check

1. How many electrons are involved in each covalent bond?

   a) 1 ✓ ✗
   b) 2 ✓
   c) 3
   d) 4

2. What are covalent structures that only have a few atoms in them called?

   Simple Covalent ✓

3. Draw a dot-and-cross diagram to show the covalent bonds in water (H_2O).

4. Why does hydrogen chloride have a low melting point?

   because its a covalent liquid compound

5. Why does hydrogen chloride not conduct electricity?

   The molecules do not carry an overall + charge

6. Why do diamond and graphite have high boiling points?

   Because they have strong covalent bonds.

CRUDE OIL: FORMATION AND SEPARATION

Formation of crude oil

The fossil fuels (coal, oil and natural gas) have resulted from the action of heat and pressure over millions of years, in the absence of air, on material from plants and animals (organic material) that has been covered by layers of sedimentary rock.

Crude oil is a mixture of a very large number of compounds.

- A **mixture** consists of two or more elements or compounds that are not chemically bonded together.
- The chemical properties of each substance in the mixture are unchanged. This makes it possible to separate the substances in a mixture by physical methods, including **fractional distillation.**

Most of the compounds in crude oil consist of molecules made of carbon and hydrogen atoms only. These compounds are called **hydrocarbons**.

Fractional distillation of crude oil

The many hydrocarbons in crude oil may be separated into fractions, each of which contains molecules with a similar number of carbon atoms, by a process called **fractional distillation**. This is carried out in a fractionating column. It works by:

1 **evaporating the oil** and

2 allowing it to **condense** at different levels in the fractionating column according to the **boiling point** of the hydrocarbon.

Smaller hydrocarbons travel further up the fractionating column. They have lower boiling points.

This diagram shows the fractions obtained from the fractional distillation of crude oil.

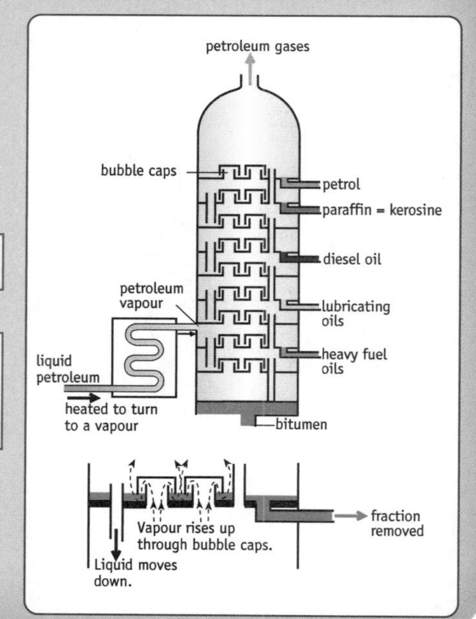

Crude oil is a fossil fuel that is obtained from the Earth's crust. Crude oil is useless on its own. It needs to be separated out into useful materials.

Uses of the fractions

Fraction	Use
Flammable gases	Bottled gas and chemicals
Petrol	Car fuel
Naphtha	Manufacture of chemicals/ pharmaceuticals
Kerosene	Jet fuel
Diesel oil	Diesel fuel
Heavy fuel oils	Fuel for ships
Bitumen	Roads and roofing felt

The hydrocarbon molecules in crude oil vary in size. The larger the hydrocarbon molecule (i.e. the greater the number of carbon atoms):

- the higher its boiling point
- the less **volatile** it is (i.e. the less easily it turns into a **vapour**)
- the less easily it flows (i.e. the more **viscous** it is)
- the less easily it **ignites** (i.e. the less **flammable** it is)

This limits the usefulness as fuels of hydrocarbons with large molecules.

Progress check

1. Describe how crude oil is formed.
2. What is a hydrocarbon?
3. How is crude oil separated?
4. On the diagram below, mark an X where the smallest molecules accumulate.

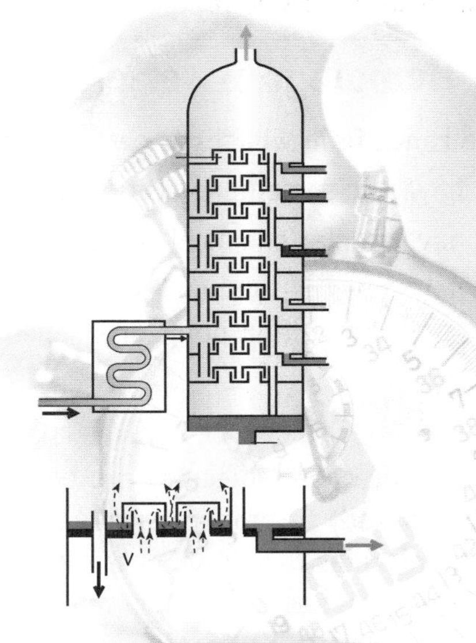

5. By what property are hydrocarbons separated in a fractionating column?

ALKANES AND CRACKING

Alkanes

Alkanes are saturated hydrocarbons.

This means that there are only single bonds in the hydrocarbon molecule. The table shows the formula and structure of the first four alkanes.

Name	Methane	Ethane	Propane	Butane
Formula	CH_4	C_2H_6	C_3H_8	C_4H_{10}
Structure	H H—C—H H	H H H—C—C—H H H	H H H H—C—C—C—H H H H	H H H H H—C—C—C—C—H H H H H
Number of carbon atoms	1	2	3	4

Homologous series

The alkanes form what is known as a **homologous series.** Members of a homologous series:

- have the same general formula (the general formula of alkanes is C_nH_{2n+2})
- have similar chemical properties
- have physical properties that gradually change as the number of carbon atoms increases (e.g. the boiling point of alkanes gradually increases)

Cracking

Large hydrocarbon molecules can be broken down (**cracked**) to produce smaller, more useful molecules. Some of these molecules are **alkanes** and some of them are **alkenes** (see page 52).

Cracking involves:

1 **heating the hydrocarbons** to vaporise them and

2 passing the vapours over a hot **catalyst**

A **thermal decomposition** reaction then occurs.

This diagram below shows how cracking can be carried out in the laboratory.

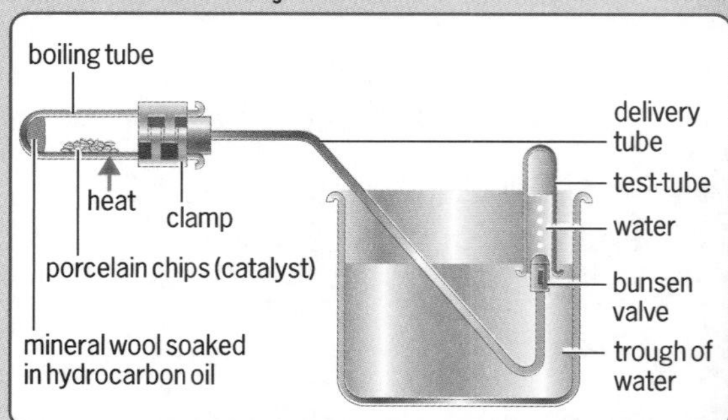

One type of hydrocarbon obtained from crude oil is called an alkane. Small alkane molecules can be used as fuels. Larger alkane molecules can be cracked to make smaller, more useful molecules.

Equations for cracking

If decane ($C_{10}H_{22}$) is cracked then the products could, for example, contain ethene (C_2H_4). You can write an equation to work out what the other product will be.

$$C_{10}H_{22} \rightarrow C_2H_4 + ?$$

The numbers of carbons and hydrogens must be the same on both sides of the equation.

There are ten C atoms on the left and only two on the right.

This means the other product must contain eight C atoms.

There are 22 H atoms on the left and only four on the right.

This means the other product must contain 18 H atoms.

Hence the other product is C_8H_{18}, i.e. octane (note that octane is an alkane because it fits the general formula C_nH_{2n+2}).

Progress check

1. What do you understand by the term 'saturated hydrocarbon'?

   It is called an alkane

2. What is the formula of propane?

   C_3H_8

3. Which alkane is represented by this structure?

```
     H   H
     |   |
 H — C — C — H
     |   |
     H   H
```

   C_2H_6 Ethane

4. What two conditions are needed to carry out cracking?

   heat + ~~water~~ a catalyst.

5. Complete the following equation for the cracking of octane.

   $C_8H_{18} \rightarrow 2C_2H_4 + ?$

   C_4H_{10}

ALKENES AND POLYMERISATION

Alkenes

Alkenes are hydrocarbons that have carbon–carbon double covalent bonds.

Alkenes are unsaturated.

These unsaturated hydrocarbons are reactive and so are useful for making many other substances.

The structure of ethene (C_2H_4)

The structure of propene (C_3H_6)

Test for alkenes

A simple laboratory test for an unsaturated hydrocarbon (i.e. an alkene) is to use bromine water. The yellow-brown **bromine water** becomes colourless as the bromine reacts with the hydrocarbon.

bromine water
result
alkane, e.g. hexane
alkene, e.g. hexene
hexane shows no change
hexene decolourises

Polymerisation

Polymers have very large molecules and are formed when many small molecules of substances called **monomers** (molecules with a double carbon–carbon bond, i.e. alkenes) join together. This process is called **polymerisation**.

During polymerisation:

- One of the bonds in the double bond breaks.
- A new bond is formed with another monomer molecule.

Alkenes are the more useful hydrocarbon found in crude oil. Their major use is in the manufacture of plastics, a process called polymerisation.

Addition polymerisation occurs when unsaturated monomers join together to form a polymer with no other substance being produced in the reaction.

Plastics are polymers made by polymerisation. For example, poly(ethene) (often called polythene) is made by polymerising the simplest alkene, ethene.

$$4\ \mathrm{H_2C{=}CH_2}$$

ethene molecules (monomers)

↓ polymerisation

$$\mathrm{-CH_2-CH_2-CH_2-CH_2-CH_2-CH_2-CH_2-CH_2-}$$

part of a poly(ethene) molecule (a polymer)

Instead of drawing out a long section of the polymer, you can show the repeating unit.

$$n\ \mathrm{H_2C{=}CH_2} \longrightarrow \mathrm{\left[-CH_2-CH_2-\right]_n}$$

ethene — poly(ethene)

Progress check

1. What do you understand by the term 'unsaturated'? reactive + useful for making other substances
2. Draw the structural formula of the molecule with the formula C_2H_4.
   H H C=C H H
3. Describe how you could distinguish chemically between a sample of octane (a liquid alkane) and octene (a liquid alkene). An alkene will reactive with water vigourously
4. What do you understand by the term 'polymerisation'?
5. Draw a section of the polymer formed when propene (C_3H_6) undergoes polymerisation (show a section of the polymer containing three monomer units).

EXTRACTION OF IRON AND ALUMINIUM

The blast furnace

The three raw materials added to the blast furnace are:

- haematite (iron ore)
- coke (pure C)
- limestone (to remove any acidic impurities)

Diagram of a blast furnace

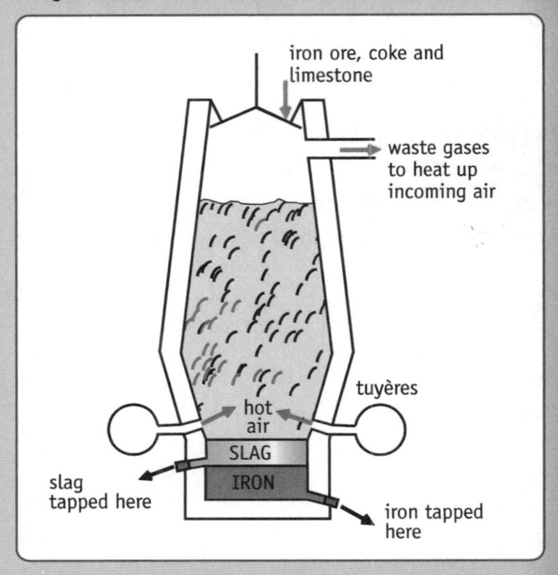

Inside the blast furnace

Carbon reacts with oxygen to form carbon dioxide.

↓

The carbon dioxide reacts with more carbon to form carbon monoxide.

↓

The carbon monoxide **reduces** the iron oxide to iron.

↓

The carbon monoxide is **oxidised** to carbon dioxide.

The limestone breaks down into calcium oxide (CaO) and carbon dioxide. The calcium oxide reacts with impurities in the haematite (mainly sand, SiO_2) to form molten **slag**.

The redox reaction forming iron

oxidation

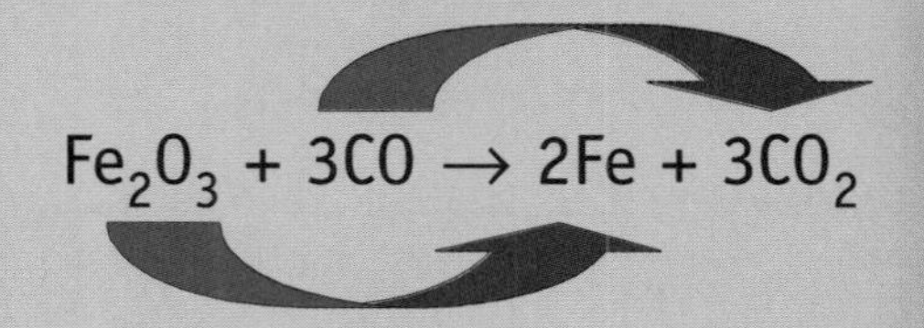

$$Fe_2O_3 + 3CO \rightarrow 2Fe + 3CO_2$$

reduction

When oxidation and reduction both occur, the reaction is described as a redox reaction.

Iron is extracted from its ore haematite (Fe_2O_3) in a blast furnace. Aluminium is a more reactive metal than carbon. It needs a more powerful method of reduction. This method is electrolysis.

Extraction of aluminium

Reactive metals such as aluminium are extracted by electrolysis.

The raw material for producing aluminium is purified **bauxite** (aluminium oxide, Al_2O_3). Aluminium oxide has a very high melting point. It is dissolved in **molten cryolite**, a compound that contains aluminium. Dissolving the purified bauxite in molten cryolite **lowers the melting point** of the aluminium oxide. This means that less heat is needed to keep the mixture molten and so energy costs are reduced.

The electrodes are made of graphite. The aluminium ions (Al^{3+}) are attracted to the negative electrode (**cathode**), where they gain electrons to form aluminium.

$$Al^{3+} + 3e^- \rightarrow Al$$

This is a **reduction** reaction. Reduction occurs when electrons are gained.

The oxide ions (O^{2-}) are attracted to the positive electrode (**anode**) where they lose electrons to form oxygen gas.

$$2O^{2-} \rightarrow O_2 + 4e-$$

This is an **oxidation** reaction. Oxidation occurs when electrons are lost.

Oxidation	Reduction
Is	Is
Loss (of electrons)	Gain (of electrons)

The oxygen formed at the anode reacts with the graphite to form carbon dioxide. This means that the anodes burn away and so need to be replaced regularly.

$$C(s) + O_2\ (g) \rightarrow CO_2\ (g)$$

Diagram of cell used for the industrial extraction of aluminium

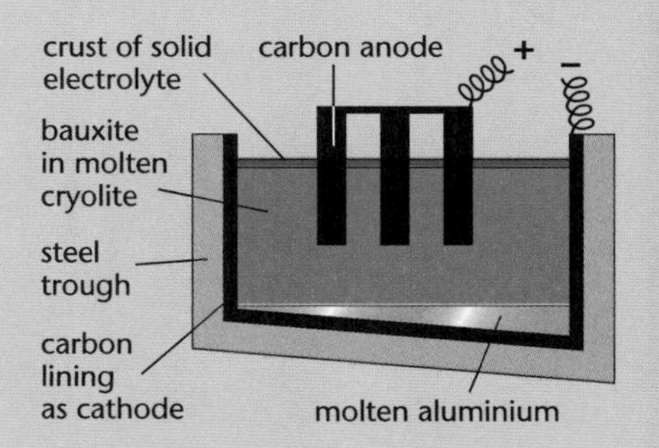

COPPER PURIFICATION AND ELECTROLYSIS OF BRINE

Purification of copper

Copper can be purified by electrolysis, using a positive electrode made of the impure copper and a negative electrode of pure copper in a solution containing copper ions.

1 The copper at the anode dissolves.

$Cu(s) \rightarrow Cu^{2+}(aq) + 2e^-$

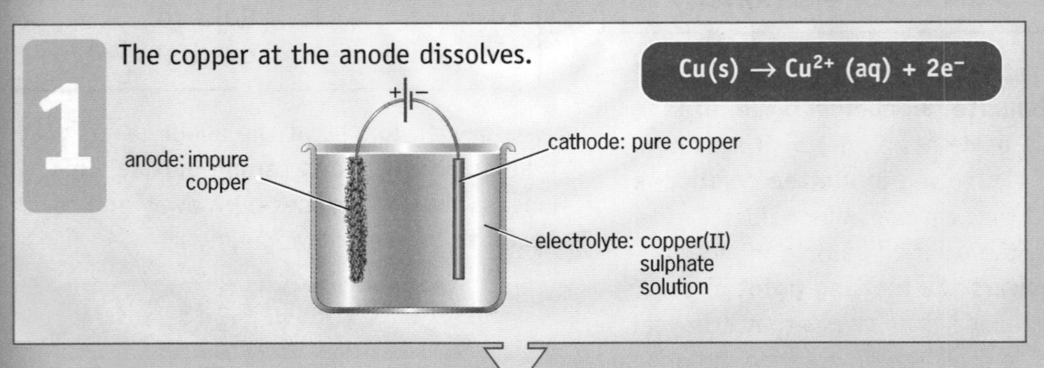

2 The copper cations are attracted to the cathode, where they gain electrons and are deposited as copper metal.

$Cu^{2+}(aq) + 2e^- \rightarrow Cu(s)$

Electrolysis of sodium chloride solution (brine)

Sodium chloride (common salt) is a compound of an alkali metal and a halogen. It is found in large quantities in the sea and in underground deposits. The electrolysis of sodium chloride solution is an important industrial process.

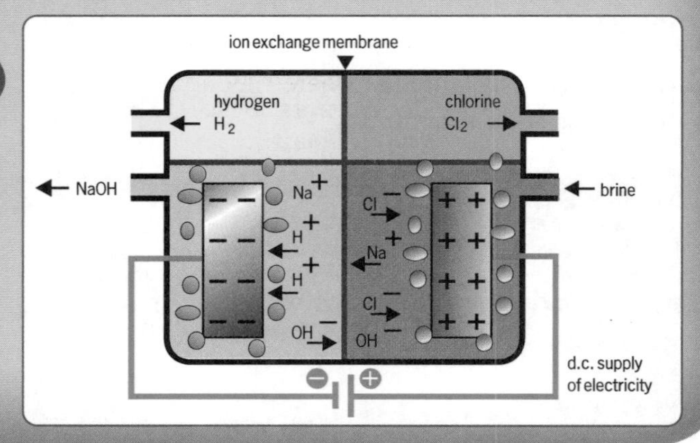

Very pure copper is a very good conductor of electricity. Mined impure copper is purified by electrolysis. Brine is a concentrated sodium chloride solution. Electrolysis of this solution produces three useful products that can be sold and used for other purposes.

The reactions occurring at each electrode are:

Cathode (negative electrode)
$2H^+ + 2e^- \rightarrow H_2$

Anode (positive electrode)
$2Cl^- \rightarrow Cl_2 + 2e^-$

The electrodes are made out of an unreactive metal – usually titanium. Titanium is used because it is a good conductor of electricity and it will not react with the chlorine gas or sodium hydroxide solution.

The products

Chlorine gas is formed at the positive electrode (anode) and **hydrogen** gas at the negative electrode (cathode). The resulting solution is **sodium hydroxide**. These three products are used to make other useful materials.

Substance	Use
Chlorine	Kills bacteria in drinking water and swimming pools. Manufacture of hydrochloric acid, disinfectants, bleach and PVC plastic.
Hydrogen	Manufacture of ammonia and margarine.
Sodium hydroxide	Manufacture of soap, paper and ceramics.

A simple laboratory **test for chlorine** is that it **bleaches damp litmus paper**.

Progress check

1. Why does copper need to be purified?

2. Label the diagram below to show how the purification of an impure piece of copper can be carried out.

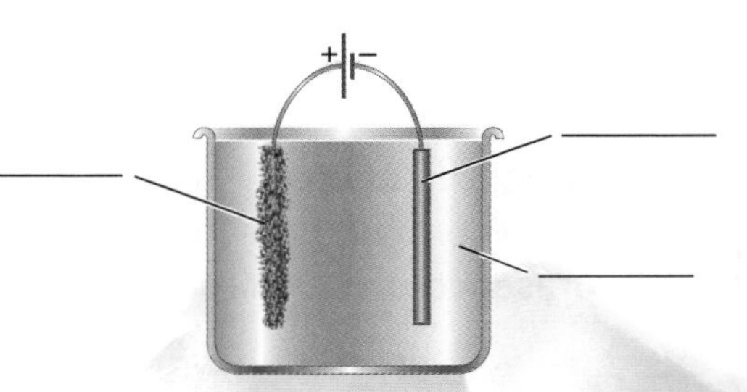

3. Balance this half-equation to show what happens at the cathode during the purification of copper.

Cu^{2+} + ___e^- → Cu

4. Name the three products formed during the electrolysis of brine.

5. Give one use for each of the products in this process.

REVERSIBLE REACTIONS AND PRODUCTION OF AMMONIA

Reversible reactions

If A and B react together to make C and D, and C and D react together to make A and B, this is a **reversible** reaction and it can be shown like this.

$$A + B \rightleftharpoons C + D$$

ammonium chloride $\rightleftharpoons$ ammonia + hydrogen chloride

white solid $\rightleftharpoons$ colourless gases

Raw materials

Ammonia is made by reacting nitrogen and hydrogen together in the presence of an iron catalyst.

nitrogen + hydrogen $\rightleftharpoons$ ammonia

$$N_2 + 3H_2 \rightleftharpoons 2NH_3$$

This is known as the Haber process.

Nitrogen is obtained from air.

Hydrogen is obtained from natural gas (methane).

The catalyst in this process is iron, thinly coated onto metal gauze to give it a greater surface area.

Conditions

The reaction conditions used in the manufacture of ammonia, chosen to produce a worthwhile yield at a reasonable rate, are:

- a temperature of 450°C
- a pressure of 200 atmospheres

On cooling the ammonia liquefies and is removed. The remaining nitrogen and hydrogen are recycled.

Why is a pressure of 200 atmospheres used?

A high pressure favours the production of ammonia because **high pressure favours the reaction that produces fewer molecules of gas**. There are four molecules of reactant gases (one nitrogen and three hydrogen) but only two molecules of product.

$$1N_2\,(g) + 3H_2\,(g) \rightleftharpoons 2NH_3\,(g)$$

1 + 3 = 4 molecules of reactant
2 molecules of product

An even higher pressure would produce more ammonia but achieving very high pressures costs more than the value of the extra ammonia produced. So a pressure of 200 atmospheres is a compromise between yield (amount of ammonia) and cost.

Reversible reactions go forwards and backwards. Ammonia (NH_3) is used in the manufacture of fertilisers, explosives and nitric acid. The formation of ammonia is a reversible reaction.

Why is a temperature of 450°C used?

The reaction to produce ammonia is **exothermic**. This means that a low temperature favours the formation of ammonia. However, if the temperature is too low then the rate of reaction will be too slow.

So the temperature chosen (450°C) is a **compromise** between yield (the amount of product) and the rate of reaction.

Uses of ammonia

Ammonia is used to make fertilisers, nitric acid and explosives.

Nitrogen containing fertilisers are made by **neutralising** ammonia with either sulphuric or nitric acid.

e.g. $NH_3 + HNO_3 \rightarrow NH_4NO_3$

ammonia + nitric acid → ammonium nitrate

The oxidation of ammonia forms nitric acid.

Progress check

1. What is meant by the term 'reversible reaction'?
2. What symbol is used to represent a reversible reaction?
3. What temperature and pressure are used in the production of ammonia?
4. Explain why these conditions are used.
5. Give one use for ammonia.

THE ROCK CYCLE

This diagram gives information about the different stages of the rock cycle.

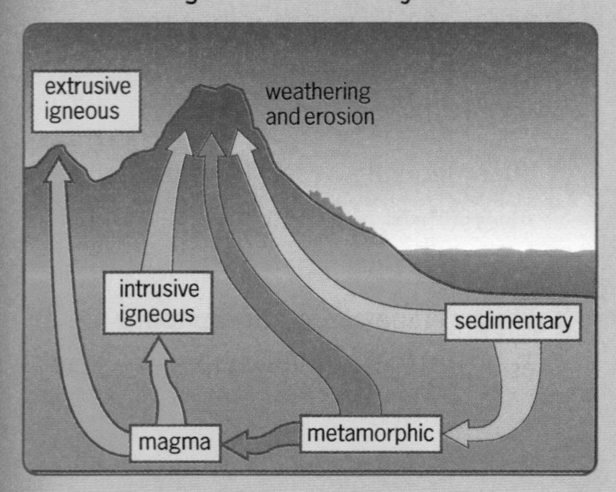

Igneous rocks

Igneous rocks are formed by the **cooling** and **solidifying** (crystallisation) of molten magma. Magma that reaches the surface of the Earth cools and solidifies more rapidly than magma that cools inside the Earth.

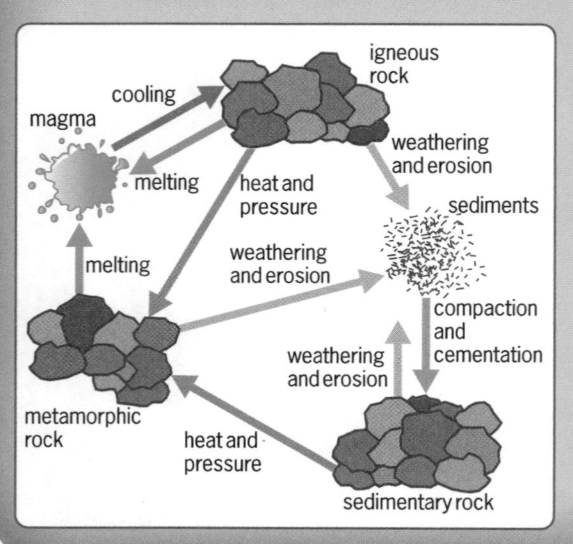

Intrusive igneous rocks (e.g. granite) are formed when magma crystallises inside the Earth's crust. **As crystallisation occurs slowly the crystals formed are large.**

Extrusive igneous rocks (e.g. basalt) are formed when magma crystallises on the Earth's surface. **As crystallisation occurs quickly the crystals formed are small.**

Weathering and erosion

Weathering is the breakdown of stationary rock. Methods of weathering include **physical**, e.g. freeze–thaw, **chemical** (acid rain etc.) and **biological** (plant root growth etc.).

Erosion occurs when broken-off bits of rock (from weathering) are further broken down by movement, e.g. by gravity as rock fragments fall down a hill or by water in streams, rivers etc.

Weathering and erosion over long periods of time turn igneous rock into small particles of rock called **sediments**.

Sedimentary rock

Eventually these sediments end up at the bottom of the sea. The **high pressure** of the sea over long periods of time compacts the sediments into sedimentary rock (e.g. limestone, mudstone). This process is called **cementation**.

The rock cycle shows how the three main types of rock are interchanging.

Sediments contain evidence of how they were deposited (e.g. layers formed by discontinuous deposition, ripple marks formed by currents or waves). At the surface of the Earth younger sedimentary rocks usually lie on top of older rocks.

Sedimentary rocks are often found tilted, folded, fractured (faulted) and sometimes even turned upside down. This shows that **the Earth's crust is unstable** and has been subjected to very large forces.

Large-scale **movements of the Earth's crust can cause mountain ranges** to form very slowly over millions of years. These replace older mountain ranges worn down by weathering and erosion.

Metamorphic rock

Metamorphic rock (e.g. marble, slate, schist) is formed by the effects of **heat** and **pressure** recrystallising other (usually sedimentary) rocks.

Metamorphic rocks are associated with the Earth's movements (**tectonic activity**) which created present-day and ancient mountain belts. They are evidence of the high temperatures and pressure created by these mountain-building processes.

Progress check

1. Name the three different types of rock.
2. What is main difference in appearance between intrusive and extrusive igneous rock?
3. What causes this difference to occur?
4. Give an example of each of biological, chemical and physical weathering.
5. What two conditions are needed for metamorphic rock to be formed?

WORKING OUT FORMULAE

Formulae

The formula of a substance simply tells you how many of each type of atom there are in a compound. The formula of water is H_2O. This means that in a molecule of water there are two atoms of hydrogen and one atom of oxygen.

To work out the formula of a compound you need to know about the electron configuration of each atom present.

Water contains hydrogen atoms and oxygen atoms.

Hydrogen has the electron configuration: 1

Remember, all atoms want to have a full outer shell of electrons so an atom of hydrogen wants to gain one electron. We say that hydrogen has a **valency** of 1.

Oxygen has the electron configuration: 2,6

Oxygen wants to gain two electrons so oxygen has a valency of 2.

To work out the formula of water simply write the atoms showing their valencies like this:

$H^1 \; O^2$

Then swap the valencies like this ...

$H^1 \; O^2$

$H_2 \; O_1$

If you follow the arrows then this gives you the formula H_2O_1. You do not usually write the '1' so the formula simply becomes H_2O.

Example

Work out the formula of aluminium sulphide.

The electron configuration of Al is 2,8,3 so an atom of aluminium wants to lose three electrons, i.e. its valency is 3.

The electron configuration of sulphur is 2,8,6 so an atom of sulphur wants to gain two electrons, i.e. its valency is 2.

$Al^3 \; S^2$

$Al_2 \; S_3$

Hence, the formula of aluminium sulphide is Al_2S_3.

Formulae involving complex ions

The above examples were for compounds containing two elements. Complex ions contain two or more atoms. The table below shows the formulae of the common complex ions.

Formula of ion	Valency	Name of ion
OH^-	1	Hydroxide
NO_3^-	1	Nitrate
SO_4^{2-}	2	Sulphate
CO_3^{2-}	2	Carbonate
NH_4^+	1	Ammonium

An important skill at GCSE is the ability to be able to write down the formula of a substance. With a small amount of practice this can easily be mastered.

With complex ions it is important to remember that the charge on the ion applies to the whole ion.

The formula can be worked out as it was before but because the charge applies to the whole ion, put brackets around the atoms of the complex ion before you swap the valencies.

Example

The formula of calcium hydroxide

$Ca^2 \; (OH)^1$

$Ca_1 \; (OH)_2$

Hence, the formula is $Ca(OH)_2$.

Example

The formula of ammonium sulphate

$(NH_4)^1 \; (SO_4)^2$

$(NH_4)_2 \; (SO_4)_1$

In the above formula you can remove the brackets from around the SO_4 because the number there is 1. Hence, the formula of ammonium sulphate becomes:

$(NH_4)_2SO_4$

Progress check

Work out the formula of each of these compounds:

1. sodium oxide
2. magnesium chloride
3. carbon sulphide
4. sodium carbonate
5. lithium nitrate
6. aluminium hydroxide

HOW TO USE THE QUIZ CARDS

There are several stages to successful revision – one of the most important is writing a list of the topics you need to know.

Then it's all about working through these essential topics, making useful notes and learning the key facts.

This is where these quiz cards can help you.

The questions on the cards provide a last-minute check of some key GCSE facts.

- You can leave them in the book and refer to them when you want
- You can tear them out and keep them handy for testing yourself
- You can get someone else to test you
- You can test your friends, which is also a good way of helping information sink in
- You can add to the cards by making your own sets of questions and answers

Remember – PREPARATION and PRACTICE and you'll be on the way to a good result!

What process is responsible for the following reactions?

glucose → ethanol + carbon dioxide
carbon dioxide + water → glucose + oxygen
glucose → lactic acid
glucose + oxygen → carbon dioxide + water

What is the equation for photosynthesis?

Use this list to complete the equation:

glucose water oxygen carbon dioxide light

a) Which enzyme in saliva breaks down starch into sugar?
b) Pepsin in gastric juice acts in the stomach, breaking down what to amino acids?
c) Lipase in pancreatic juice acts in the small intestine, breaking down fats/oils to what?

Which part of the heart performs each of these tasks?

a) Brings deoxygenated blood into the right atrium
b) Makes sure that the blood goes in one direction only
c) Takes oxygenated blood from the lungs to the left atrium
d) Takes blood from the left ventricle to most of our organs

The diagram shows part of the abdomen of a person. Can you name each part?

urethra vena cava
aorta ureter
bladder

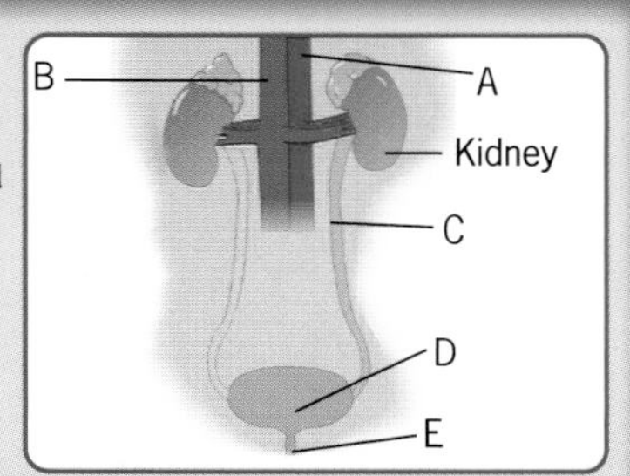

Complete the passage. Each gap needs two words:
.... such as coal are burned.
.... is given off into the air.
This gas diffuses into clouds and mixes with
.... This forms ....
and comes back towards the Earth's surface as acid rain.

Use the words from the list to complete the passage.

product substrate active site broken down

An enzyme has an ....
A .... molecule fits into the active site and is then .... to form .... molecules.

Why do the alkali metals (group 1) become more reactive as you go down the group?

Explain why ionic compounds do not conduct electricity when they are solid but do when molten or aqueous.

Calculate the empirical formula of the substance that contains 1.1 g of boron and 10.65 g of chlorine.

$$carbon\ dioxide + water \xrightarrow{light} glucose + oxygen$$

Did you put oxygen and carbon dioxide on the correct sides of the equation?

Anaerobic respiration
Photosynthesis
Anaerobic respiration
Aerobic respiration

a) Vena cava
b) Valve
c) Pulmonary vein
d) Aorta

a) Amylase (carbohydrase)
b) Proteins
c) Fatty acid and glycerol

Fossil fuels such as coal are burned. **Sulphur dioxide** is given off into the air. This gas diffuses into clouds and mixes with **water vapour**. This forms **sulphurous acid** and comes back towards the Earth's surface as acid rain.

A – aorta
B – vena cava
C – ureter
D – bladder
E – urethra

As the atoms get larger the force of attraction between the nucleus and the outer shell electron decreases. Hence, less energy is needed to remove the electron and so reactivity increases.

An enzyme has an **active site**. A **substrate** molecule fits into the active site and is then **broken down** to form **product** molecules.

BCl_3

In a solid the ions are not mobile (because they are only able to vibrate). When molten or aqueous the ions are free moving.

Write a word equation for the reaction between zinc and copper oxide.
Explain why the reaction occurs.

Calculate the mass of water produced when 6 g of hydrogen burns.

$$2H_2 + O_2 \rightarrow 2H_2O$$

Draw the repeating unit formed from the polymerisation of this monomer.

```
H       H
 \     /
  C = C
 /     \
H       H
```

How is sedimentary rock converted into metamorphic rock?

This shows light travelling from water towards the water/air boundary. What is the name given to the angle *c*?

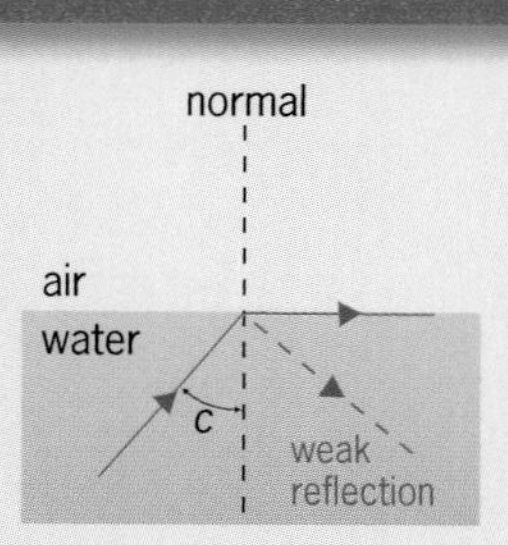

There are two mistakes in this circuit. What are they?

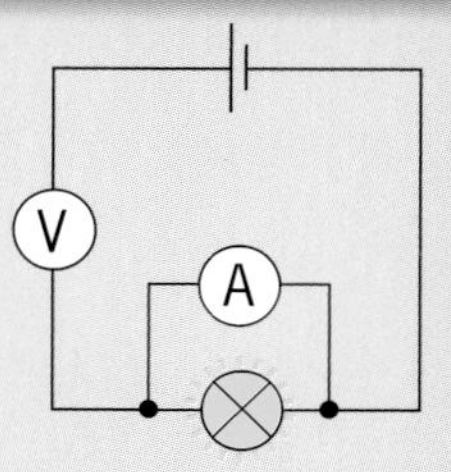

Some domestic smoke detectors contain a radioactive source emitting alpha-particles. What are alpha-particles?

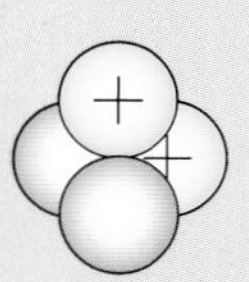

All the galaxies in our Universe are flying apart from each other. What does this tell us about our Universe?

Two cars A and B are travelling along a straight road. The graphs show the distance against time graphs for the cars. Which car has the greater velocity?

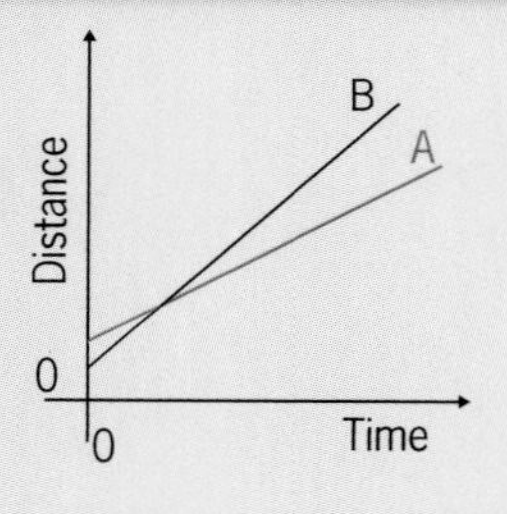

A balloon is rubbed with a dry duster and it acquires a positive charge. What is the charge on the duster?

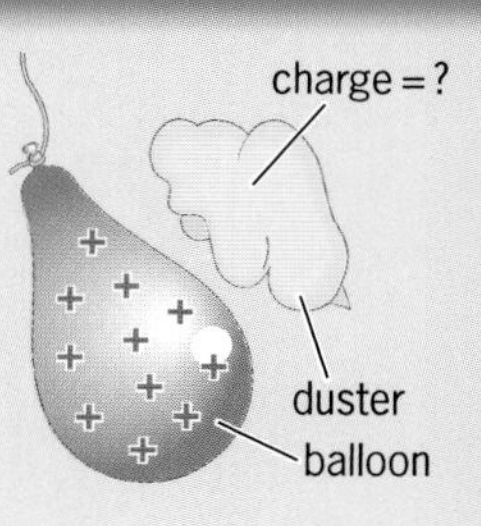

54 g

zinc + copper oxide → zinc oxide + copper

Zinc is more reactive than copper so it displaces the copper in copper oxide.

Movements in the Earth's surface cause the sedimentary rock to be exposed to high pressures and high temperatures which changes sedimentary rock into metamorphic rock.

$$\left[\begin{array}{ccc} & H & H \\ & | & | \\ - & C - & C - \\ & | & | \\ & H & H \end{array}\right]_n$$

The ammeter should be in series and the voltmeter should be in parallel.

Critical angle

The Universe is expanding.

Helium nuclei emitted from unstable nuclei

The duster has negative charge.

The car B has a greater velocity.

EXAM TECHNIQUE

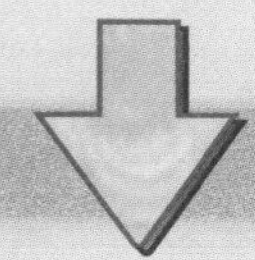

FOLLOW OUR CHECKLIST TO HELP YOU BEFORE AND DURING THE EXAMS

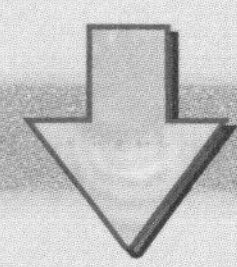

Preparation

Use the time before the exams effectively. Write a list of all the topics you have to cover. Work through your notes systematically and ask for help with any topics that you're struggling to understand.

Practice

Attempt as many practice questions and past papers as possible. Familiarise yourself with the question types, the marks allocated and the time allowed. Compare your marks to those given in the mark schemes – see where you did well and where there is room for improvement.

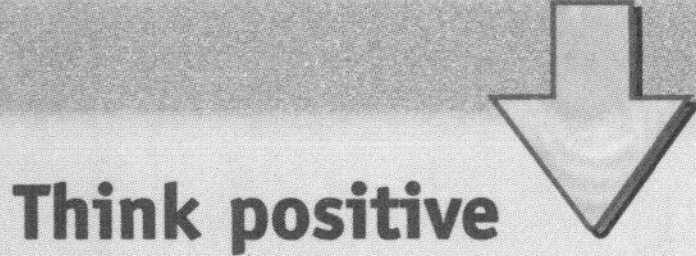

Think positive

Even if time is running short, remind yourself of the progress you have made. Use what time is left by working through the key topics – either those that are most likely to come up in the exam or those that you find most difficult.

IN THE EXAM ITSELF...

- Follow all the instructions in the exam paper
- Attempt the correct number of questions
- Read each question carefully and more than once

- Highlight the key words in the question and note the command word – State, Describe, Explain, Discuss, Find, Suggest, Calculate, List etc.
- Check the number of marks available for each question and answer accordingly

- Plan your response in brief note form
- Ensure that you answer the question asked and that your response stays relevant
- Allocate time carefully and make sure you complete the paper

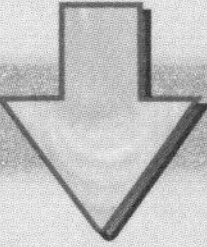

- Return to any questions you have left out and read through your answers at the end
- Remember that accurate spelling and good use of English do count

We hope this book will help you on the way to GCSE success.

BALANCING EQUATIONS

Consider the following equation: $Al + Cl_2 \rightarrow AlCl_3$

It does not balance because there are different numbers of each type of atom on either side of the equation.

STEP 1

Under each substance in the equation draw a box.

Al	+	Cl_2	→	$AlCl_3$
[ ]	+	[ ]	→	[ ]

STEP 2

In each box write the correct numbers of atoms of each element in the substance.

Al	+	Cl_2	→	$AlCl_3$
Al		ClCl		AlClClCl

Remember that the number by an element tells you how many atoms of that element are present.

STEP 3

Count up all the atoms in the boxes! There must be the same number of atoms of each element on both sides of the equation. You can add as many boxes as you like but you are not allowed to put things in or take things out of a box.

Al	+	Cl_2	→	$AlCl_3$
Al		ClCl		AlClClCl

The numbers of Al atoms already balance but there are three Cl atoms on the right but only two on the left, so add another box of Cl_2 to the left!

Al	+	Cl_2	→	$AlCl_3$
Al		ClCl		AlClClCl
		ClCl		

Many students think that balancing equations is impossible! To overcome this, use the technique on these pages for balancing equations.

There are now four Cl atoms on the left but only three on the right, so add another box of $AlCl_3$ to the right.

Al	+	Cl_2	→	$AlCl_3$
Al		ClCl		AlClClCl
		ClCl		AlClClCl

Now there are six Cl atoms on the right but only four on the left so add another box of Cl_2 to the left.

Al	+	Cl_2	→	$AlCl_3$
Al		ClCl		AlClClCl
		ClCl		AlClClCl
		ClCl		

Now the Cl balances. However, there are now two Al atoms on the right but only one on the left. Add one more box of Al on the left.

Al	+	Cl_2	→	$AlCl_3$
Al		ClCl		AlClClCl
Al		ClCl		AlClClCl
		ClCl		

The equation now balances! To write the balanced equation you simply count up the number of boxes.

$$\mathbf{2}Al + \mathbf{3}Cl_2 \rightarrow \mathbf{2}AlCl_3$$

Progress check

Balance these equations.

1. $Ca + O_2 \rightarrow CaO$
2. $Cr + HCl \rightarrow CrCl_3 + H_2$
3. $CH_4 + Cl_2 \rightarrow CCl_4 + HCl$
4. $Na + O_2 \rightarrow Na_2O$
5. $P + Br_2 \rightarrow PBr_3$
6. $Al + O_2 \rightarrow Al_2O_3$

MOLE CALCULATIONS 1

Mass of atoms and molecules

Atoms of different elements have different masses. To be able to work out exactly what is happening in chemical reactions you need to know how the masses of atoms compare with each other, i.e. their **relative atomic masses** (A_r).

The relative atomic mass of an atom is the mass of an atom compared to the mass of an atom of carbon.

When you want to know the relative atomic mass of an atom you just use the **mass number** (large number) on the periodic table (you are provided with a periodic table in the exam).

The **relative formula mass** (M_r, sometimes called the relative molecular mass) of a molecule is found by adding together the individual atomic masses of the atoms in a compound.

Examples

For HF the M_r is:

$1 + 19 = 20$

For $CaCO_3$ the M_r is:

$40 + 12 + (3 \times 16) = 100$

Percentage of an element in a compound

The percentage of an element in a compound is found by working out:

$$\frac{\text{number of atoms of that element} \times A_r}{M_r} \times 100\%$$

Many students find mole calculations difficult. Learn to follow a few simple steps and, with lots of practice, you will find them much easier!

Example

Calculate the percentage of calcium in calcium oxide (CaO).

$\frac{1 \times 40}{56} \times 100\% = 71\%$

Empirical formula calculations

The empirical formula of a compound is the simplest whole-number ratio of atoms in a compound.

You will be given the masses of elements that are present in a compound. You can find the empirical formula in two steps.

1 Divide each mass by the A_r (this is the number of moles).

2 Divide each of the above answers by the smallest answer in **1**.

Example

Calculate the empirical formula of a compound that contains 2.8 g of silicon and 3.2 g of oxygen.

	Si	**O**
Mass (g)	2.8	3.2
1) moles		
= mass ÷ A_r	2.8 ÷ 28	3.2 ÷ 16
=	0.1	0.2
2) ÷ 0.1	0.1 ÷ 0.1	0.2 ÷ 0.1
=	1	2

Hence, the empirical formula is SiO_2.

Progress check

1. Calculate the relative formula mass of:
   i. MgO
   ii. H_2SO_4
   iii. $Na_2S_2O_3$

2. Using your answers to question 1, work out the percentage by mass of:
   i. oxygen in MgO
   ii. sulphur in H_2SO_4
   iii. sodium in $Na_2S_2O_3$

3. Calculate the empirical formula of:
   i. a compound containing 1.4 g of lithium and 1.6 g of oxygen
   ii. a compound containing 0.28 g of silicon and 1.42 g of chlorine

MOLE CALCULATIONS 2

10 MINS

1
2
3
DAY 4
5
6
7

Calculating masses from equations

You can use the mass of either a product or a reactant in an equation to work out the mass of a product formed or reactant needed. To do this you also need a balanced symbol equation.

Follow these steps.

1. Work out M_r for each substance (this will be the same as A_r for elements). Write this under each species in the equation. If a substance has a number before it in the balanced equation then multiply A_r or M_r accordingly.
2. Under the appropriate substance write down the mass given in the question.
3. Work out the ratio between the value in step 1 and step 2 by dividing the value in step 1 by the value in step 2.
4. Divide the value for the substance you are interested in by the value obtained in step 3.

This is complicated! Use the worked examples that follow to apply the above steps.

Example

Calculate the mass of carbon dioxide formed if 6 g of carbon reacts with oxygen.

$C (s) + O_2 (g) \rightarrow CO_2 (g)$

	C	**O_2**	**CO_2**
Step 1	12	32	44
Step 2	6		
Step 3	12 ÷ 6 = 2		
Step 4			44 ÷ 2 = 22

Hence, the answer to the question is **22 g**.

Questions involving reacting masses are common at GCSE. Again, if you follow the steps and practise lots of questions then you will get much better at them!

Example

Calculate the mass of phosphorus trichloride (PCl_3) made if 3.1 g of phosphorus reacts with chlorine.

$2P\ (s) + 3Cl_2\ (g) \rightarrow 2PCl_3\ (s)$

	$2P$	$3Cl_2$	$2PCl_3$
Step 1	62	213	275
Step 2	3.1		
Step 3	62 ÷ 3.1 = 20		
Step 4			275 ÷ 20 = 13.75

Answer = 13.75 g

Calculating volumes of gases from equations

This method can also be used to work out the volumes of gases produced during a reaction. You need to know that the relative formula mass of any gas has a volume of 24 000 cm^3 (this is Avogadro's law).

In the first example in the previous section you can work out the volume of carbon dioxide produced.

This is because M_r for carbon dioxide is 44 g. This means 44 g of CO_2 will occupy a volume of 24 000 cm^3.

The answer to the question was that 22 g of carbon dioxide was formed. Now, 22 is half of 44, therefore half of 24 000 cm^3 gas was formed, i.e. 12 000 cm^3.

Progress check

1. Calculate the mass of calcium chloride that can be made from reacting 5 g of calcium with chlorine.

   $Ca + Cl_2 \rightarrow CaCl_2$

2. Calculate the mass of sodium oxide that is made when 5.75 g of sodium is reacted with oxygen.

   $4Na + O_2 \rightarrow 2Na_2O$

3. Calculate the mass of aluminium that is needed to make 6 g of aluminium oxide.

   $4Al + 3O_2 \rightarrow 2Al_2O_3$

4. Calculate the volume of oxygen that is needed to make 8 g of magnesium oxide.

   $2Mg + O_2 \rightarrow 2MgO$

THE PERIODIC TABLE 1

GROUP

transition metals

PERIOD	1	2											3	4	5	6	7	0
1	H																	He
2	Li	Be											B	C	N	O	F	Ne
3	Na	Mg											Al	Si	P	S	Cl	Ar
4	K	Ca	Sc	Ti	V	Cr	Mn	Fe	Co	Ni	Cu	Zn	Ga	Ge	As	Se	Br	Kr
5	Rb	Sr	Y	Zr	Nb	Mr	Tc	Ru	Rh	Pd	Ag	Cd	In	Sn	Sb	Te	I	Xe
6	Cs	Ba	La	Hf	Ta	W	Re	Os	Ir	Pt	Au	Hg	Tl	Pb	Bi	Po	At	Rn
7	Fr	Ra	Ac															

Group 1 elements – the alkali metals

The alkali metals:

- are metals with a low density (the first three are less dense than water and therefore float on water)
- react with non-metals to form ionic compounds in which the metal ion will have a charge of +1
- form compounds that are white solids and that dissolve in water to form colourless solutions
- react with water releasing hydrogen
- form hydroxides (OH) that dissolve in water to give alkaline solutions

Reactivity of group 1 metals

In group 1, the further down the group an element is:

- **the more reactive the element**
- **the lower the melting point and boiling point**

Reaction with water

When a piece of lithium, sodium or potassium is placed in cold water the metal floats, may melt and moves around the surface of the water. The metal reacts with the water to form a metal hydroxide solution and hydrogen gas.

An understanding of the trends and patterns in the periodic table is important if you are to understand the chemical reactions of the elements.

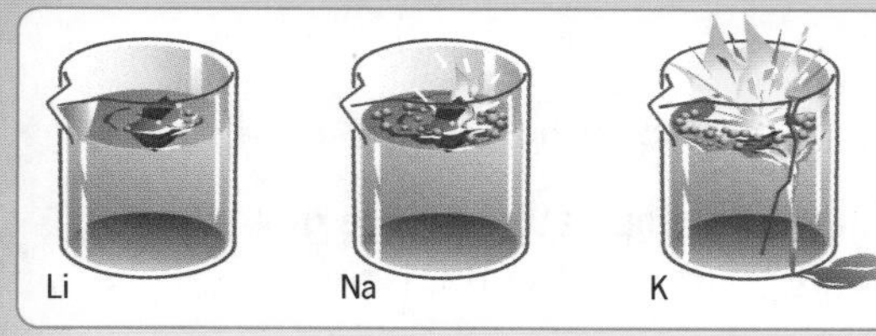

alkali metal + water → metal hydroxide + hydrogen

For example, using sodium as an example:

$2Na (s) + 2H_2O (l) \rightarrow 2NaOH (aq) + H_2 (g)$

The more reactive the metal, the more vigorous is the reaction with water.

Reactivity increases as you go down group 1 because:

The atoms get larger.

↓

Therefore the outer electron becomes further away from the nucleus.

↓

Therefore there is less attraction between the nucleus and the electron.

↓

Therefore it becomes easier for the atom to lose the outer electron and hence it is more reactive.

Transition metals

In the centre of the periodic table is a block of metallic elements. These elements, which include iron and copper, are known as **transition metals**.

Like all other metals, transition metals are good conductors of heat and electricity and can easily be hammered or bent into shape.

Compared to alkali metals, transition metals:

- have high melting points (except for mercury which is a liquid at room temperature)
- are hard, tough and strong
- are much less reactive and so do not react (corrode) as quickly with oxygen and/or water

These properties make transition metals very useful as **structural materials** (e.g. iron, usually in the form of steel) and for making things that must allow heat or electricity to pass through them easily (e.g. copper for electrical cables and water pipes).

Most transition metals form **coloured compounds**. These can be seen:

- in pottery glazes of various colours
- in weathered copper (green)

Many transition metals are used as **catalysts**, e.g. iron in the Haber process and platinum in the manufacture of nitric acid.

THE PERIODIC TABLE 2

Non-metals

The elements in group 7 and group 0 have the typical properties of non-metals.

- They have low melting points and boiling points (at room temperature all the group 0 elements are gases, the first two group 7 elements are gases and the third, bromine, is a liquid).
- They are brittle and crumbly when solid.
- They are poor conductors of heat and electricity even when solid or liquid.

Group 7 – the halogens

The elements in group 7 of the periodic table (known as the halogens):

- have coloured vapours (chlorine is green, bromine is red, iodine is purple)
- consist of molecules that are made up of pairs of atoms
- form ionic salts with metals, in which the chloride, bromide or iodide ion (halide ions) carries a charge of –1
- form molecular compounds with other non-metallic elements

Reactivity of the halogens

In group 7, the further down the group an element is:

- the less reactive the element
- the higher its melting point and boiling point

A more reactive halogen can displace a less reactive halogen from an aqueous solution of its salt.

chlorine + potassium iodide → potassium chloride + iodine

$Cl_2 + 2KI_{(aq)} \rightarrow 2KCl_{(aq)} + I_2$

Reactivity increases as you go up group 7 because:

The atoms get smaller.

↓

Therefore the outer shell is closer to the nucleus.

↓

Therefore there is stronger attraction between the nucleus and the electron in another atom.

↓

Therefore the atom is more able to attract that electron and so it is more reactive.

Approximately a quarter of the elements are non-metals. They are found on the right-hand side of the periodic table.

Group 0 – the noble gases

Group 0 elements:

- are all chemically very unreactive gases
- exist as individual atoms rather than diatomic gases (like most other gaseous elements)
- are used as inert gases in filament lamps and in electrical discharge tubes (e.g. fluorescent lighting)

The first element in the group, helium, is much less dense than air and is used in balloons.

Reactivity of the noble gases

Group 0 elements are unreactive and monatomic because their outer shell of electrons is full, so atoms have no tendency to gain, lose or share electrons.

Progress check

1. What is the trend in reactivity of the group 1 metals?
2. Explain this trend.
3. Write a word equation for the reaction between sodium and water.
4. Give two typical properties of non-metals.
5. Write 'true' or 'false' after each of the following statements.
   i. Chlorine gas has a yellow/green colour.
   ii. The halogens exist as single atoms.
   iii. Chlorine is less reactive than bromine.
   iv. Noble gases exist as single atoms.
   v. Noble gases are more reactive than the halogens.
6. Explain why neon is such an unreactive gas.
7. Complete the following equation.

   sodium iodide + bromine →
8. Explain why bromine is more reactive than iodine.

RATES OF REACTION

10 MINS

Factors affecting rates

The speed (rate) of a chemical reaction increases:

- if the temperature increases
- if the concentration of dissolved reactants or the pressure of gases increases
- if solid reactants are in smaller pieces (greater surface area)
- if a catalyst is used

Catalysts

Catalysts work by lowering the activation energy of the reactant molecules and this allows the reaction to happen more easily.

A catalyst increases the rate of a chemical reaction without being used up during the reaction.

A catalyst is used over and over again to speed up the conversion of reactants to products. Different reactions need different catalysts.

Collision theory

Chemical reactions can only occur when reacting particles collide with each other and with sufficient energy. The minimum amount of energy particles must have to react is called the **activation energy**. If they collide with the activation energy then a successful collision occurs.

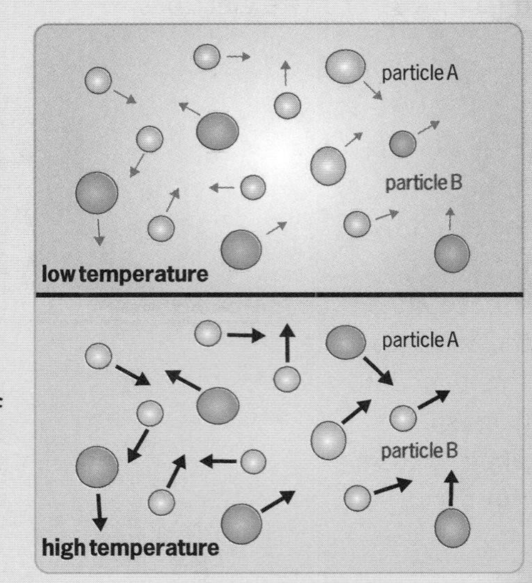

Collision theory and temperature

Increasing the temperature increases the speed of the reacting particles so that they collide more frequently and with more energy (i.e. more particles will possess the activation energy). This increases the rate of reaction.

Collision theory can be used to explain rates of reaction.

Collision theory and concentration

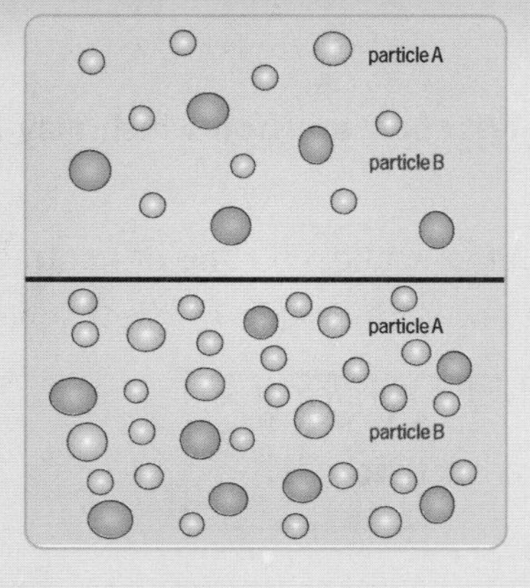

Increasing the concentration of reactants in solutions and increasing the pressure of reacting gases also increases the frequency of collisions and so increases the rate of reaction.

The lower diagram shows a higher concentration of reactions and hence there are more collisions.

Collision theory and surface area

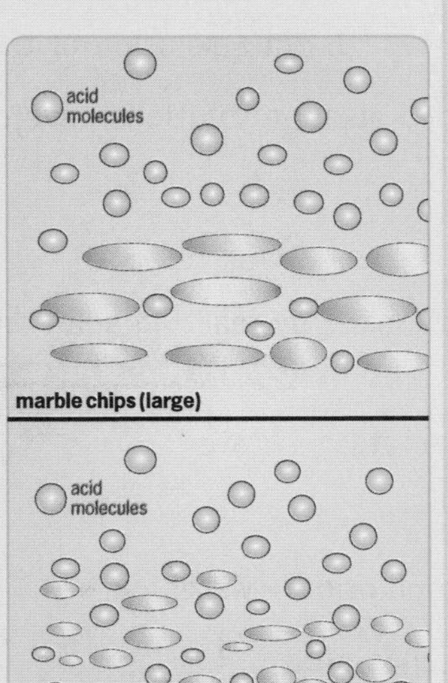

If one of the reactants in a reaction is a solid then the rate of reaction can be increased by increasing the surface area of the solid reactant. This provides more spaces where collisions can occur.

Progress check

1. What must particles possess if a successful collision is to occur?
2. Give two reasons why increasing the temperature increases the rate of a chemical reaction.
3. Explain why doubling the concentration of a reactant should theoretically double the rate of a reaction.
4. Why does using smaller marble chips in the reaction with hydrochloric acid result in a greater rate of reaction than if larger chips are used?

ACIDS, ALKALIS AND SALTS

Acidity and indicators

When a substance dissolves in water it forms an **aqueous solution** which may be **acidic**, **alkaline** or **neutral**. Water itself is neutral.

Indicators can be used to show whether a solution is acidic, alkaline or neutral by the way their colours change.

The pH scale is used to show how acidic or alkaline a solution is.

pH	1	2	3	4	5	6	7	8	9	10	11	12	13	14
Colour	Red		Orange		Yellow			Green			Blue		Violet	
Strength	strong ACIDS ←				weak		neutral	weak		→ ALKALIS strong				

The colours show the colour of **universal indicator** (UI) in a solution of that pH.

An indicator can be used to show when acidic and alkaline solutions have completely reacted to form a neutral salt solution.

Salts

Compounds of alkaline metals called **salts** can be made by reacting solutions of their hydroxides (which are alkaline) with acids. These are **neutralisation reactions**.

acid + metal hydroxide solution → neutral salt solution + water

For example:

hydrochloric acid + sodium hydroxide → sodium chloride + water

The particular salt produced in any reaction depends on:

- the acid used
- the metal used in the alkali

Many chemical reactions involve the reactions of acids and alkalis. When an acid is reacted with an alkali, a neutralisation reaction has occurred.

Neutralising **hydrochloric acid** produces **chlorides.**

Example

lithium hydroxide + hydrochloric acid → lithium chloride + water

$$LiOH + HCl \rightarrow LiCl + H_2O$$

Neutralising **nitric acid** produces **nitrates.**

Example

sodium hydroxide + nitric acid → sodium nitrate + water

$$NaOH + HNO_3 \rightarrow NaNO_3 + H_2O$$

Neutralising **sulphuric acid** produces **sulphates.**

Example

potassium hydroxide + sulphuric acid → potassium sulphate + water

$$2KOH + H_2SO_4 \rightarrow K_2SO_4 + 2H_2O$$

Ammonia (NH_3) also dissolves in water to produce an alkaline solution. This can be neutralised with acids to produce **ammonium salts.**

Example

ammonia solution + sulphuric acid → ammonium sulphate

$$2NH_3 + H_2SO_4 \rightarrow (NH_4)_2SO_4$$

Reactions of acids

There are four different types of reactions of acids.

1 acid + alkali → salt + water

For example: sulphuric acid + sodium hydroxide → sodium sulphate + water

$$H_2SO_4 + 2NaOH \rightarrow Na_2SO_4 + H_2O$$

2 acid + metal → salt + hydrogen

For example: hydrochloric acid + magnesium → magnesium chloride + hydrogen

$$2HCl + Mg \rightarrow MgCl_2 + H_2$$

3 acid + metal carbonate → salt + carbon dioxide + water

For example: nitric acid + calcium carbonate → calcium nitrate + carbon dioxide + water

$$2HNO_3 + CaCO_3 \rightarrow Ca(NO_3)_2 + CO_2 + H_2O$$

4 acid + metal oxide → salt + water

For example: sulphuric acid + copper oxide → copper sulphate + water

$$H_2SO_4 + CuO \rightarrow CuSO_4 + H_2O$$

EXOTHERMIC AND ENDOTHERMIC REACTIONS

Exothermic and endothermic energy changes

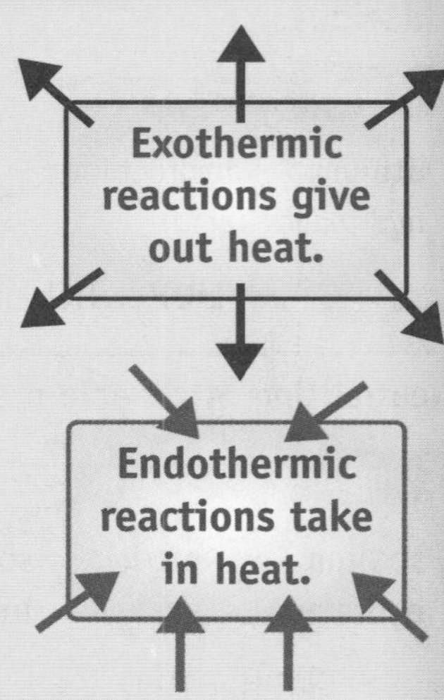

When fuels burn, energy is released as heat. Whenever chemical reactions occur, energy is usually transferred to or from the surroundings.

An **exothermic** reaction is one that transfers energy, often as heat, to the surroundings. An **endothermic** reaction is one that takes in energy, often as heat, from the surroundings.

If a reversible reaction is exothermic in one direction it is endothermic in the opposite direction. The same amount of energy is transferred in each case.

Example

blue hydrated copper(II) sulphate + heat $\rightleftharpoons$ white anhydrous copper(II) sulphate + water

The reverse reaction can be used as a test for water, i.e. anhydrous copper sulphate + water. The white anhydrous copper sulphate turns blue if water is present.

During a chemical reaction:

- energy must be supplied to break bonds
- energy is released when bonds are formed

In an **exothermic reaction**, the **energy released** from forming new bonds is greater than the energy needed to break existing bonds.

In an **endothermic reaction**, the **energy needed** to break existing bonds is greater than the energy released from forming new bonds.

Most chemical reactions involve a change in energy. This energy is in the form of heat.

Energy level diagrams

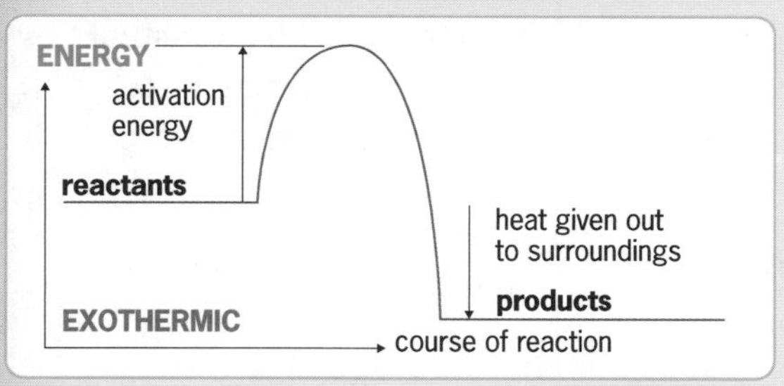

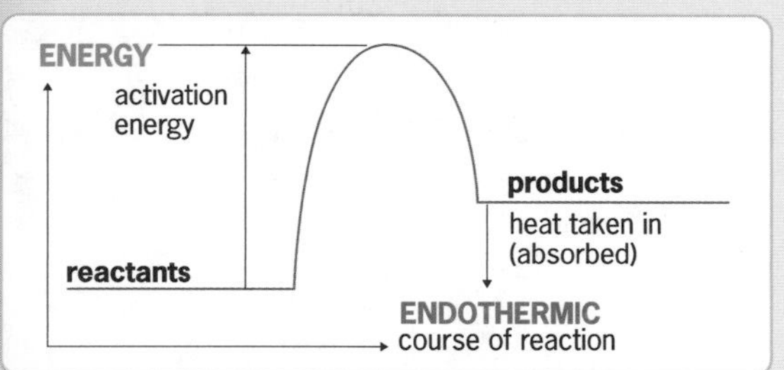

Adding a catalyst to a reaction lowers the activation energy for the reaction and so the energy level diagrams will look like the following ones.

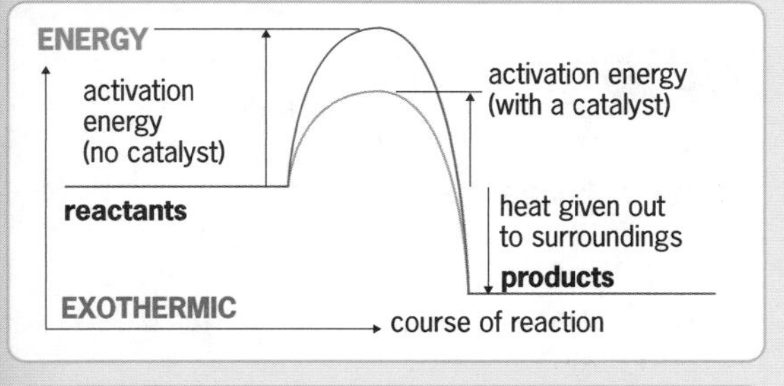

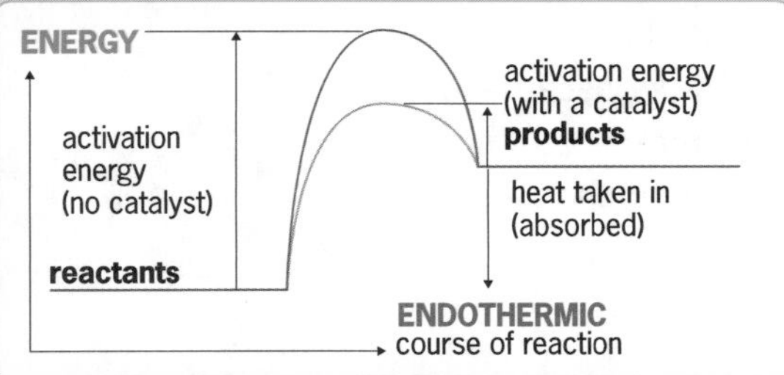

Progress check

1. What do you understand by the term 'exothermic'?
2. Draw an energy profile to show an exothermic reaction. Include the following labels.
   - reactants
   - products
   - activation energy

SPEED, VELOCITY AND ACCELERATION

15 MINS

Speed

The **speed** of an object is a measure of how quickly it covers a certain distance. It tells us how **fast** or how **slowly** an object is travelling. The speed v of an object is given by the equation:

$$\text{speed} = \frac{\text{distance travelled}}{\text{time taken}} \qquad v = \frac{d}{t}$$

where d is the distance travelled by the object in a time t.

You can use a **formula triangle** to remember the equation above.

Use your finger to cover the quantity that you need. The triangle then shows the equation or the formula.

Speed is measured in metres per second (m/s or m s^{-1}).

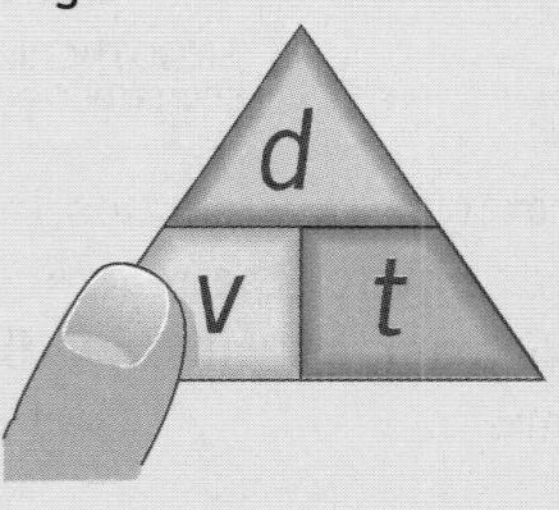

Example

A cheetah covers a distance of 200 m in a time of 6.3 s. What is the speed of the cheetah?

$$\text{speed} = \frac{\text{distance travelled}}{\text{time taken}}$$

$$\text{speed} = \frac{200}{6.3} = 31.7\ \text{m/s}$$

$$\text{speed} \approx 32\ \text{m/s}$$

Velocity

The velocity of an object tells you the instantaneous speed of the object and the direction in which it is travelling.

The speed of an object is regardless of the direction in which it is travelling but the velocity must always have the direction specified.

Examples

An aeroplane travelling at 180 m/s due north.

A satellite orbiting the Earth. The speed of the satellite remains the **same**, but its velocity **changes** because its instantaneous direction of travel changes.

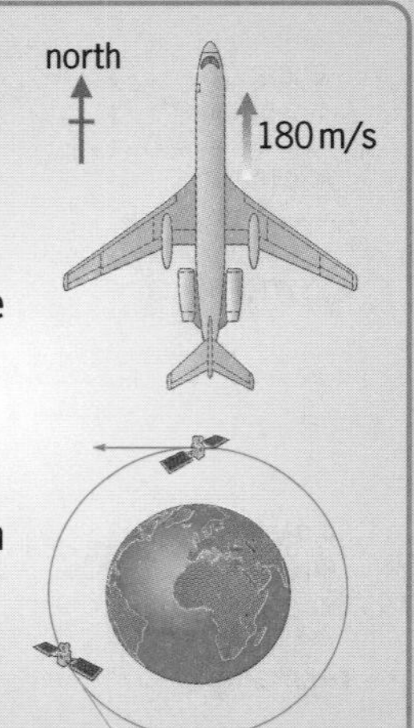

DAY 5

What is the difference between the motion of a cheetah attacking its prey and a person walking to their local shop? It is their speed.

Acceleration

The **acceleration** of an object tells you how quickly its velocity is changing. The **acceleration** of an object is given by the equation:

$$\text{acceleration} = \frac{\text{change in velocity}}{\text{time taken}}$$

$$a = \frac{\Delta v}{t}$$

where Δv is the change in the velocity of the object in a time t. The symbol Δ (delta) is used to mean 'change in'.

Acceleration is measured in m/s^2 (often written as $m\,s^{-2}$).

Example

A car starts from rest and travels in a straight line.
After 3.5 s its speed is 44 m/s. What is its acceleration?

$\Delta v = 44 - 0 = 44\,m/s$ $\quad t = 3.5\,s$

$a = \frac{\Delta v}{t}$ $\quad a = \frac{44}{3.5} = 12.6\,m/s^2$

Deceleration

Deceleration is the term used when an object's speed decreases in the direction of travel.

A **negative acceleration** means that an object is decelerating or slowing down.

Progress check

1. Which one of these is the correct unit for speed?

   ms $\quad$ $m\,s^{-1}$ $\quad$ s/m

2. Use the triangle formula to write an equation for time t.

3. Calculate the speed of a snail that travels a distance of 12 cm in 300 s.

4. Calculate the distance travelled by sound in 2.5 s. The speed of sound is 340 m/s.

5. What is the major difference between speed and velocity?

USING GRAPHS TO DESCRIBE MOTION

Distance against time graphs

Suppose an object travels along a straight line. Its distance is measured from the starting point. This distance is known as the **displacement** of the object.

For a distance against time graph, the distance travelled by the object is plotted on the vertical (y) axis and the time along the horizontal (x) axis.

The gradient of a distance against time graph is equal to the speed of the object.

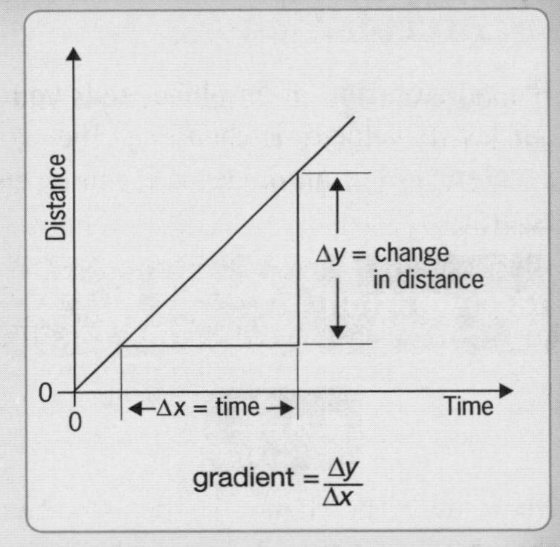

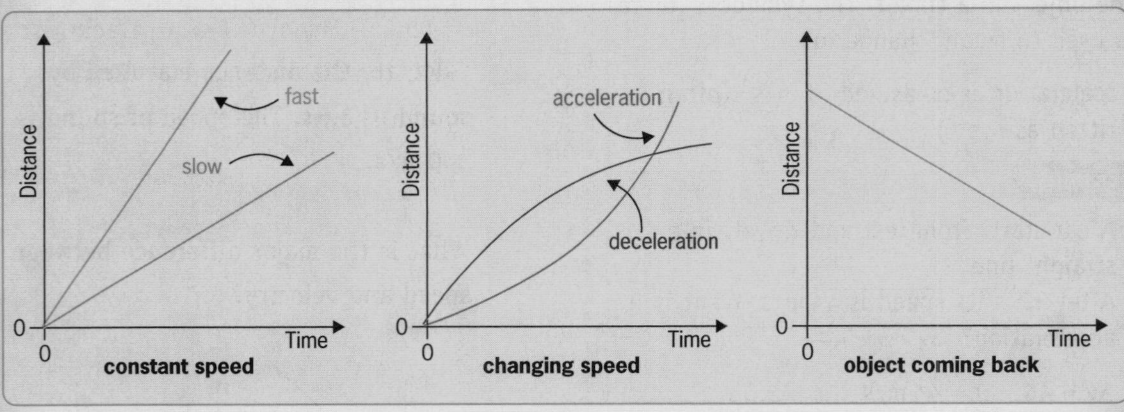

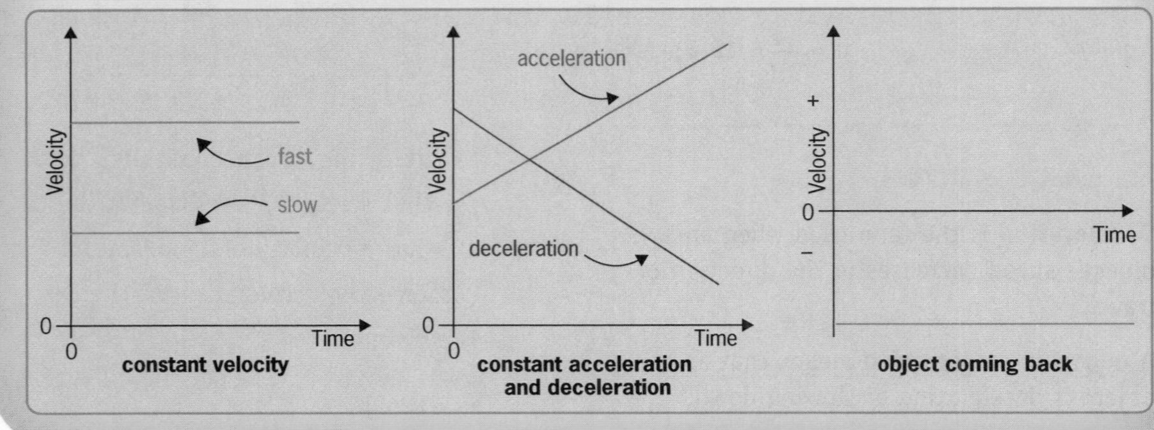

It is quite helpful to use graphs to describe the motion of an object. Two of the most helpful graphs are the distance against time graph and the velocity against time graph.

Velocity against time graphs

Suppose an object travels along a straight line. In a velocity against time graph, the velocity of the object is plotted on the vertical (y) axis and the time along the horizontal (x) axis.

A **negative** velocity means that the object is travelling in the opposite direction.

The gradient of a velocity against time graph is equal to the acceleration of the object.

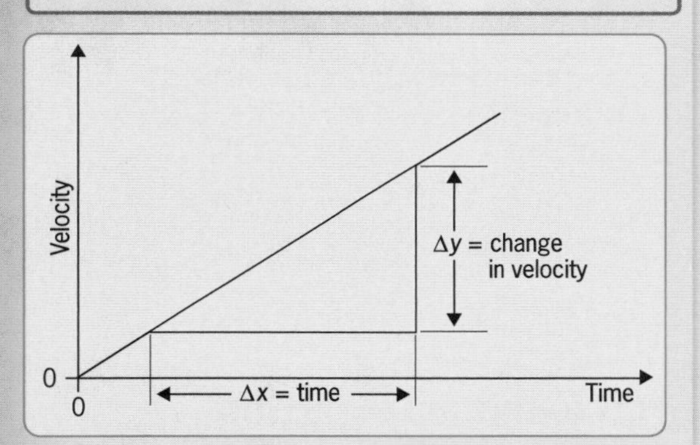

The area under a velocity against time graph is equal to the distance travelled by the object.

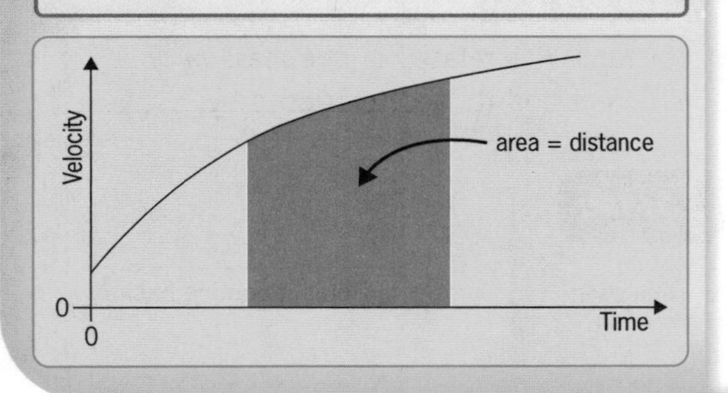

Progress check

1. What is the gradient equal to for a distance against time graph?
2. What is the gradient equal to for a velocity against time graph?
3. What does the area under a velocity against time graph represent?
4. Calculate the speed of a parachutist with the distance against time graph shown.

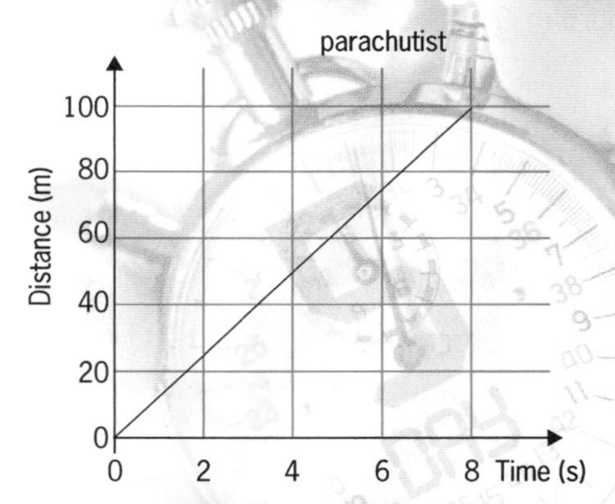

5. Calculate the distance travelled by a car that starts from rest and after 10 s has a velocity of 22 m/s. (Assume the acceleration of the car is constant.)

FORCE AND ACCELERATION

10 MINS

Balanced forces

What happens when two equal-sized forces act in opposite directions on an object?

- The object may remain stationary.
- The object may carry on moving at a constant velocity in a straight line.
- The object will have no acceleration.

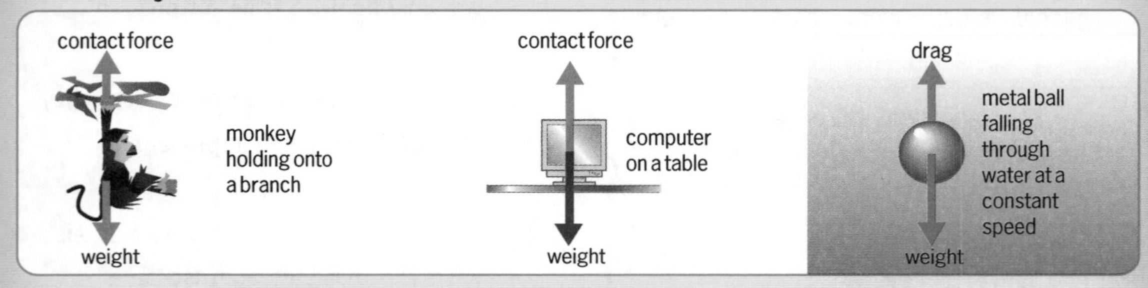

If the forces acting on an object are **balanced**, then its motion is not affected.

You can use the following alternatives to the term 'balanced forces':

- **net** force = 0
- **resultant** force = 0

Unbalanced forces

What happens when an object experiences an **unbalanced** force and the net force is not zero?

- The velocity of the object can change.
- The object can change direction.
- The object accelerates.

Force and acceleration

An object accelerates when it experiences an unbalanced force. The **acceleration** of the object depends on its **mass** and the **force acting** on it.

The net force F is related to the mass m of the object and its acceleration a by:

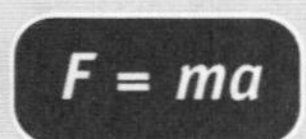

$$F = ma$$

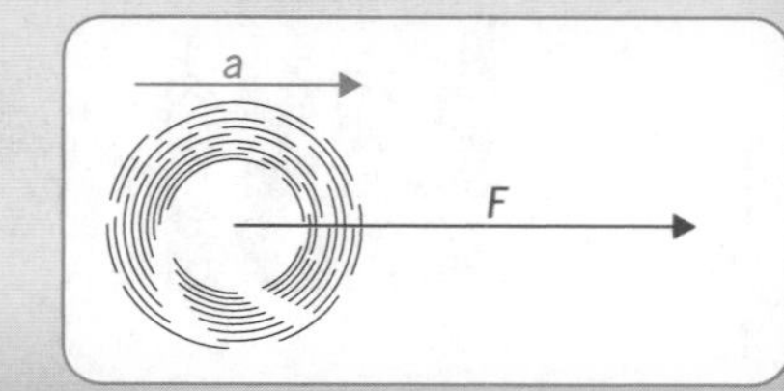

An apple falling off a tree accelerates towards the Earth's surface. It accelerates because there is a force acting on the apple. The force acting on the apple is its weight.

Example

Calculate the acceleration of the skydiver shown in the diagram.

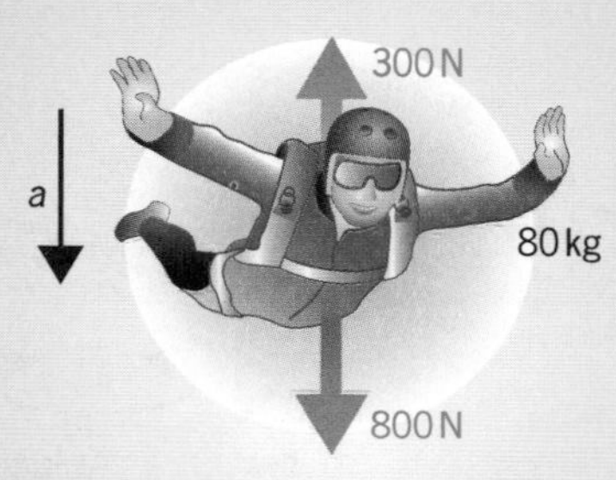

net force = 800 − 300 = 500 N

$F = ma$

$a = \frac{F}{m} = \frac{500}{80} = 6.25\ \text{m/s}^2$

acceleration ≈ $6.3\ \text{m/s}^2$

Weight

The **mass** of an object remains constant.

The **weight** of the object depends on where it is.

The weight W of an object in newtons (N) is given by the equation:

$$W = mg$$

where m is the mass of the object in kilograms (kg) and g is the acceleration of free-fall or the gravitational field strength. Close to the Earth's surface, $g = 10\ \text{m/s}^2$ or $g = 10\ \text{N/kg}$.

Progress check

1. The forces acting on an object are balanced. Can it accelerate?

2. What is the net force acting on an object that has balanced forces?

3. Determine the resultant force on a 0.80 kg bird hurtling towards the ground with an acceleration of $3.0\ \text{m/s}^2$.

4. Determine the net force on the falling book.

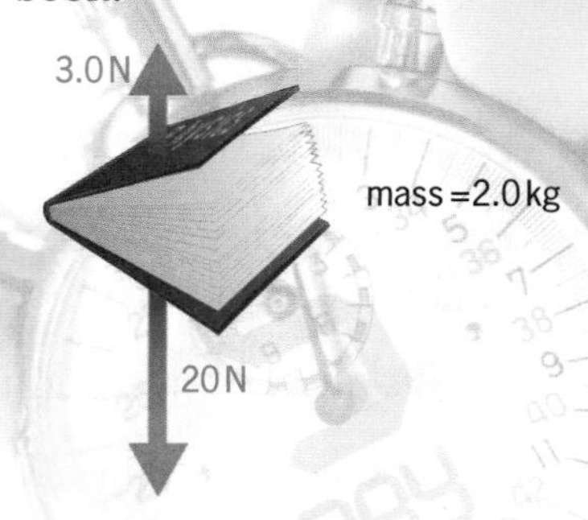

5. Calculate the acceleration of the book in Q4.

6. What is the weight of an astronaut of total mass 90 kg on Earth when he is on the surface of the Moon, where the acceleration of free-fall is $1.6\ \text{m/s}^2$?

FRICTION

Friction is a resistive force that acts against the motion of a moving object.

The friction caused by an object moving through air is known as **drag** or **air resistance**.

Friction occurs when two surfaces **rub** or **slide** against each other or when an object moves through a fluid (liquid or gas).

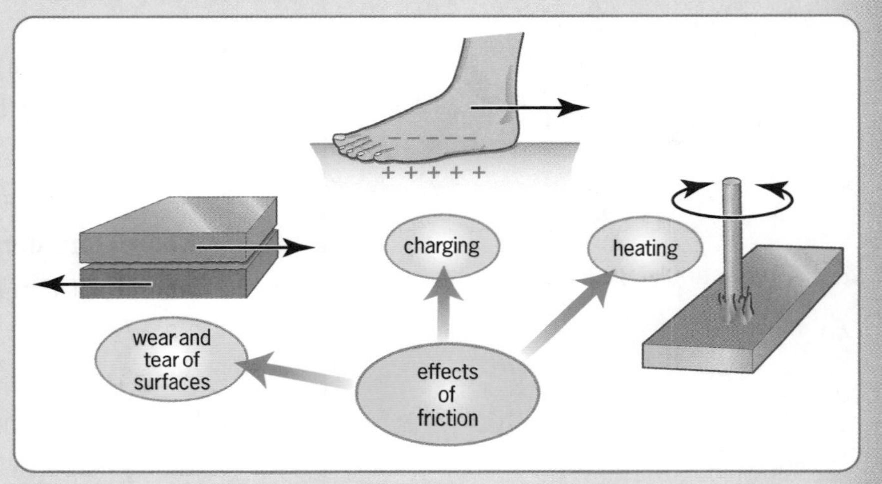

Air resistance and speed of object

The size of the **air resistance** depends on the **speed** of the object and the **area** of the object.

- Air resistance is larger for greater speeds.
- Air resistance is greater for objects with larger surface area.

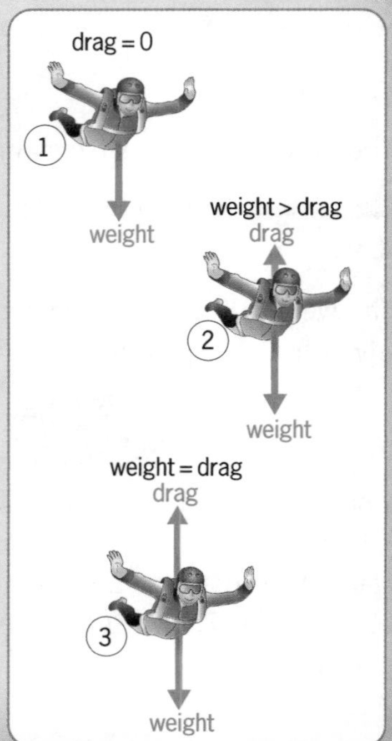

Forces on a skydiver

① The skydiver jumps off.

- The only force acting on the skydiver is his or her weight.
- The weight of the skydiver accelerates him or her in the downward direction.
- The initial acceleration of the skydiver is 9.8 m/s^2.

Without friction humans would not be able to walk. It is the friction between our shoes and the ground that enables us to move forwards.

② The size of the drag increases as the speed of the skydiver increases.

- The **net** downward force F decreases and therefore the acceleration decreases.

$$a = \frac{F}{m}$$

$$\text{acceleration} = \frac{\text{weight} - \text{drag}}{\text{mass}}$$

③ After some time, drag = weight.

- The **net** force on the skydiver is then zero.
- The **acceleration** of the skydiver is also zero.
- The skydiver travels at a **constant velocity** known as the **terminal velocity**.

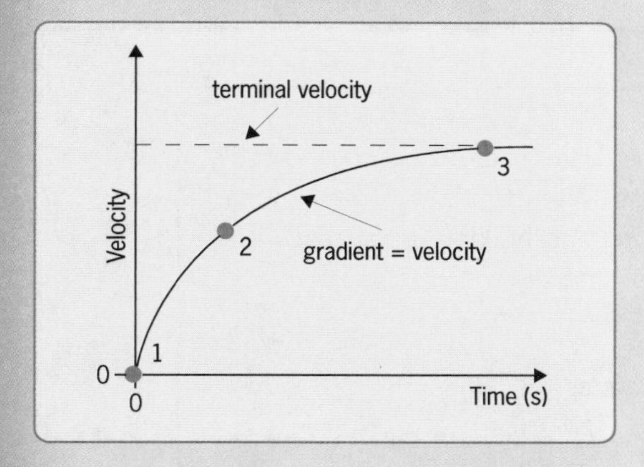

Progress check

1. What happens when an object slides or rubs against a rough surface?

2. What is the other name given to air resistance?

3. A car is travelling along a level road. What happens to the drag on the car when its speed is increased?

4. A car is travelling at a **constant** velocity of 80 km/h on the motorway. The force between the car tyres and the road surface is 2100 N.
   a) What is its acceleration?
   b) What is its terminal velocity?
   c) What is the size of the drag on the car?

5. The diagram shows the forces on a falling metal sphere. Has the sphere reached its terminal velocity?

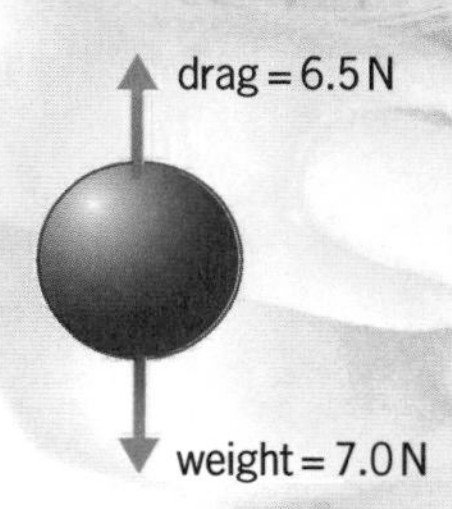

CARS AND STOPPING DISTANCES

Thinking distance

- A driver sees an obstacle on the road ahead of him. The driver takes a certain time to react before the car brakes are applied.
- The thinking distance is the **distance** travelled by the car in the time it takes for the driver to react before applying the car brakes.
- The thinking distance depends on a number of factors.

The thinking distance will increase if:

- **the speed of the car increases**
- **the driver is tired or under the influence of drugs or alcohol**

Braking distance

- The braking distance is the **distance** travelled by the car whilst the car brakes are applied and the car stops.
- The braking distance depends on a number of factors.

The braking distance will increase if:

- **the road is icy or wet**
- **the speed of the car increases**
- **the mass of the car increases**
- **the car has poor grip due to worn tyres**
- **the car has worn brake pads**

Example

A car is travelling at 15 m/s on an icy road. The driver sees a dog unexpectedly cross the road. The driver's reaction time is 0.6 s. When the brakes are applied, the car takes 5.0 s to stop. What are the thinking and braking distances?

In order to cut down on road accidents, drivers need to be alert and drive at slow speeds especially near built-up areas. A car driver would be very foolish to drive a car at high speeds when it is snowing!

distance = speed × time

thinking distance = 15 × 0.6 = 9.0 m

braking distance = area under the velocity against time graph

braking distance = $\frac{1}{2}$ × 5.0 × 15 = 37.5 m

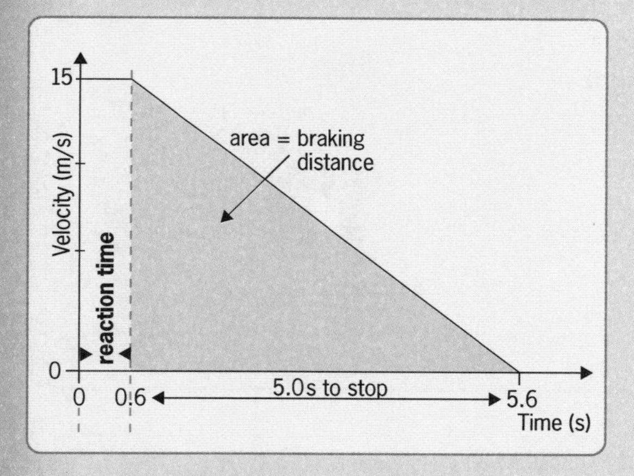

Stopping distance

stopping distance = thinking distance + braking distance

Progress check

1. *'The thinking distance is the time taken for the driver to react.'* Is this true?
2. What happens to the thinking distance if the driver is under the influence of drugs?
3. What happens to the braking distance if the road is icy?
4. Calculate the thinking distance for a car travelling at 20 m/s, if the reaction time of the driver is 0.8 s.
5. Calculate the braking distance and the stopping distance for the car in Q4, given that it takes a total time of 4.5 s to stop.

WORK DONE, ENERGY AND POWER

Work done

Work is done on an object when it **moves** as a result of a force applied to it. No work is done on an object if it does not move in the direction of the force.

To determine the amount of work done, use this equation.

work done = force × distance moved by the object in the direction of the force

$W = F \times d$

Work (W) done is measured in joules (J).

Example

A man lifts a sack of cement of weight 200 N up a ladder. The sack is raised through a vertical height of 12 m. What is the work done on the sack?

force applied on sack = weight = 200 N

$W = F \times d$ $\quad W = 200 \times 12 = 2400$ J

work done = 2.4 kJ

Energy transfer and work done

The work (W) done on an object is **converted** or **transformed** into energy. For example:

- The work done in pushing a car on a level road is converted to **kinetic energy** of the car.
- The work done in lifting a drink can is converted into **gravitational potential energy**.
- The work done by a car's brakes to stop the car is converted into **heat** or **thermal energy**.

- **Work done is measured in joules (J).**
- **Energy is also measured in joules (J).**

In physics, words such as 'work done' and 'power' have specific meanings. For example, you do no physical work whilst sitting on a chair. However, work is done when you raise yourself from the chair.

Power

Power is a measure of how quickly work is done or how quickly energy is transferred.

To determine the amount of work done, use these equations.

$$\text{power} = \frac{\text{work done}}{\text{time}}$$

$$\text{power} = \frac{\text{energy transferred}}{\text{time}}$$

- Power is measured in **watts** (W).

Example

A girl of weight 500 N runs up a small hill. She climbs a vertical height of 90 m in a time of 3.0 minutes. Calculate the power developed by the girl.

work done = $F \times d$

work done = $500 \times 90 = 45\ 000$ J

time = $3.0 \times 60 = 180$ s

$$\text{power} = \frac{\text{work done}}{\text{time}}$$

$$\text{power} = \frac{45\ 000}{180} = 250\,\text{W}$$

Progress check

1. A person is holding a book without moving it. Is there any work done on the book?

2. Calculate the work done by a builder lifting a 200 N load through a vertical height of 20 m.

3. A cyclist suddenly slams on the brakes and comes to rest. What happens to all the work done by the brakes to stop the cyclist?

4. In a weight-lifting competition, a competitor lifts a 700 N log through a vertical distance of 2.0 m in a time of 0.5 s. What is the power developed by the weight-lifter?

5. A horse can develop an average power of 800 W. How much work can the horse do in period of 5.0 minutes?

TYPES OF ENERGY

Energy transfer

The total amount of energy remains the same. It is conserved. Energy cannot be 'lost', it is simply transformed into a different form of energy. For example:

Solar cell: light → electrical energy

Coal fire: chemical energy → heat and light

According to the principle of conservation of energy, energy cannot be created or destroyed.

Different forms of energy:

- light
- heat
- sound
- electrical energy
- nuclear energy
- elastic strain energy
- kinetic energy
- gravitational potential energy

Kinetic energy

A moving object has **kinetic energy**. The kinetic energy of a moving object depends on its **mass** and on its **speed**.

The kinetic energy *E* of an object of mass *m* travelling at a speed *v* given by the equation:

$$E = \frac{1}{2}mv^2$$

Example

Calculate the kinetic energy of a car of mass 800 kg travelling at a 12 m/s.

$$E = \frac{1}{2}mv^2$$

$$E = \frac{1}{2} \times 800 \times 12^2 = 57\,600 \text{ J}$$

A car travelling at high speed brakes suddenly. What happens to its energy? Energy is not 'lost'. The car's energy is transformed mainly into heat and sound. Did you know that the total amount of energy remains the same?

Gravitational potential energy

A person lifts a heavy box from the ground onto a shelf. The person has to do work on the box. The work done on the box is transformed into 'stored' energy known as **gravitational potential energy**.

The gravitational potential energy of an object is due to its 'position' in the Earth's gravitational field.

The gravitational potential energy E of an object of mass m at a height h above the ground is given by the following equation:

$$E = mgh$$

where g = gravitational field strength for the Earth (approximately 10 N/kg).

Example

Calculate the gravitational potential energy of a 120 g apple at a height of 3.2 m above the ground.

$E = mgh$

$E = 0.120 \times 10 \times 3.2 = 3.8$ J
(Don't forget to convert the mass to kg.)

Progress check

1. What is the energy transformation for an exploding firework?
2. *'Kinetic energy is due to the position of an object above the ground.'* Is this true?
3. Calculate the kinetic energy of a 0.080 kg ball thrown at a speed of 15 m/s.
4. What is the gravitational potential energy of a person of mass 60 kg sitting on a wall at a height of 1.5 m above the ground? (g = 10 N/kg)
5. The person in Q4 jumps off the wall. What is her kinetic energy just before impacting with the ground?

STATIC CHARGE AND CURRENT

15 MINS

Static electricity

Electric charge is either positive or negative.

Insulating materials acquire a charge either by **gaining** or **losing** electrons:

- A material that **gains** electrons becomes **negatively** charged.
- A material that **loses** electrons becomes **positively** charged.

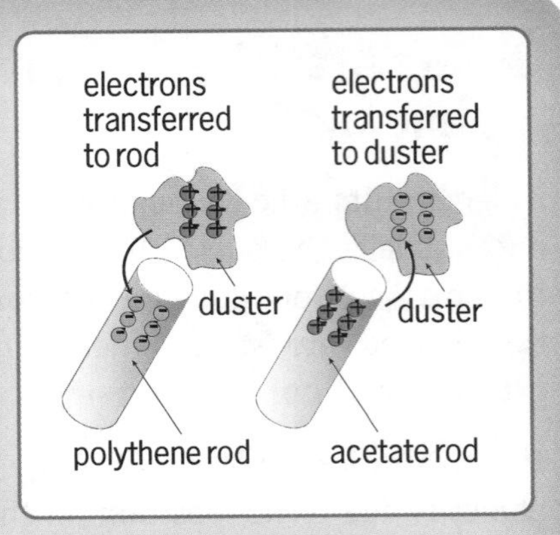

When a polythene rod is rubbed with a duster, electrons are transferred from the duster to the polythene rod. Therefore, the duster has a positive charge and the polythene a negative charge. The duster and the polythene acquire **equal but opposite** charges.

Electric current

An **electric current** is the **flow of charge**.

There is a current in a metal wire that is connected to a cell. In a **metal** the current is due to the flow of **free electrons** within the metal.

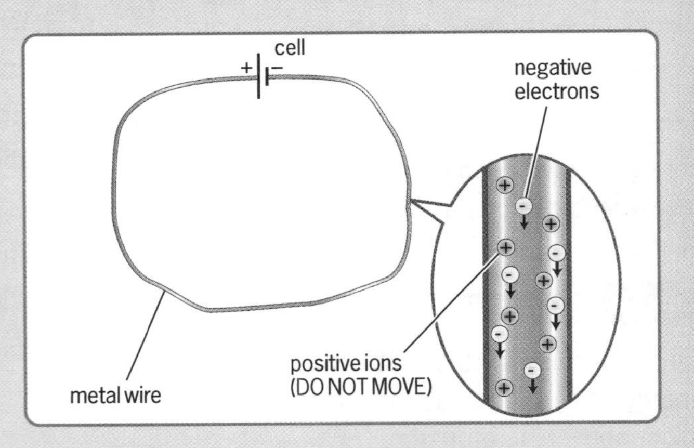

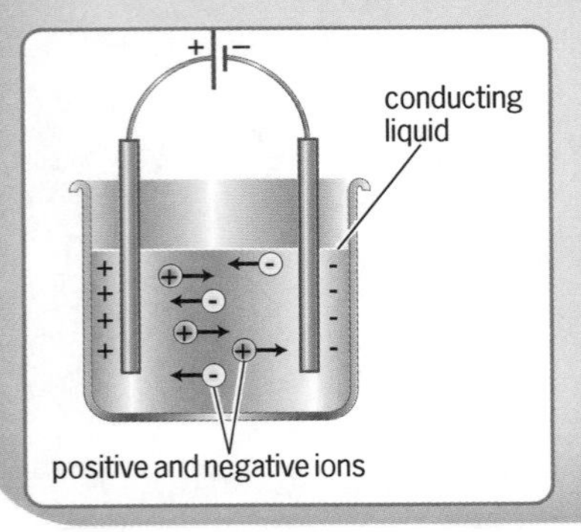

In **conducting liquids**, known as **electrolytes**, the particles responsible for the current are the positively and negatively charged **ions** within the liquid.

When some materials are rubbed against each other, an electric charge builds up on the surfaces and this can lead to an electric spark. Lightning is an example of this.

Ammeters

An ammeter is a device used to measure the current at a point in a circuit.

An ammeter is always connected in **series** with any component.

The current in a series circuit is the **same** at all points.

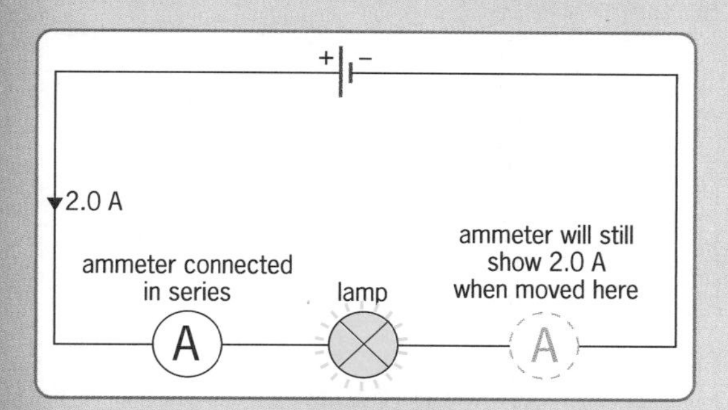

Current and charge

Electric current I is given by the equation:

$$I = \frac{Q}{t}$$

where Q is the charge flowing past a point in the circuit in a time t.

- **Charge Q is measured in coulombs (C).**
- **Time t is measured in seconds (s).**
- **Electric current I is measured in amperes or amps (A).**

Progress check

1. How can you charge two insulators?
2. Name the particles responsible for electric current in a metal.
3. What is the unit of electric current?
4. Is it true that $1\ A = 1\ C\,s^{-1}$?
5. An ammeter is used to measure the current in a resistor. How should it be connected in the circuit?
6. Calculate the current in a circuit given that in a time of 100 s the charge flow is 120 C.

VOLTAGE AND RESISTANCE

1 2 3 4 5 DAY 6 7

Voltage and potential difference

A current-carrying wire has a voltage across its ends. Another term used for voltage is **potential difference** (p.d.). The greater the current in a wire, the greater is the voltage across its ends.

12 V

12v

12v

The voltage across each lamp is the same and is equal to 12 V.

Voltmeters

The voltage across a component is measured using a voltmeter.

A voltmeter is placed across or in **parallel** with the component.

The voltage across two components connected in parallel is always the **same**.

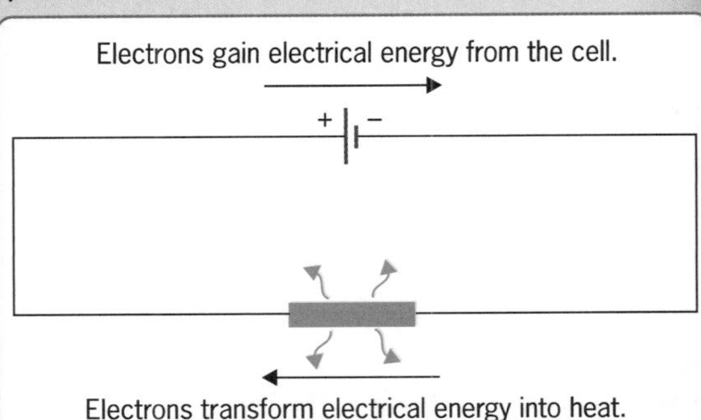

Voltage and energy transfer

The **voltage** across a component is a measure of the amount of **energy transferred per unit charge** flowing through the component.

Within the cell shown in the diagram, chemical energy is changed into electrical energy.

Electrons moving through the cell gain electrical energy.

When the electrons travel through a component, they change electrical energy into other forms such as heat, light, sound.

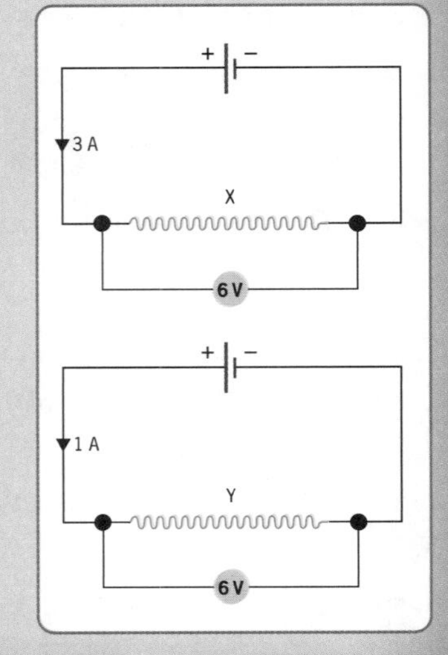

Resistance

All electrical components have resistance. Good electrical insulators, such as plastics, have a high resistance and good electrical conductors, such as metals, have a low resistance.

Two resistance wires **X** and **Y** are connected to the same battery (so that the potential difference across each is the same).

The current in the wire **X** is larger and the current in the wire **Y** is smaller. The wire **X** has a smaller resistance than wire **Y**.

large resistance → small current (for a given voltage)

Why is it important to have a plastic covering around the cable of an appliance like an electric kettle? Plastic is an electrical insulator.

Determining resistance

The **electrical resistance** R of a component is calculated by using the equation:

$$R = \frac{V}{I}$$

where V is the potential difference (voltage) across the component and I is the current in the component.

Electrical resistance is measured in ohms (Ω).

You can use a **formula triangle** to remember the equation.

You can use the circuit below to find the electrical resistance of a component.

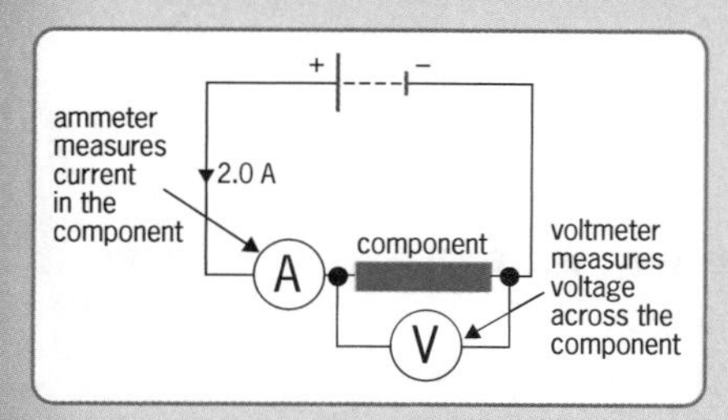

- The ammeter measures the current I in the component.
- The voltmeter measures the voltage V across the component.
- The resistance is given by the equation:

$$R = \frac{V}{I}$$

Progress check

1. What is another name for potential difference (p.d.)?
2. What is the unit for voltage?
3. What is the unit for resistance?
4. What two quantities do you need to determine the resistance of a component in a circuit?
5. Component **A** is connected to a supply. The current in it is 2.0 A. Another component **B** is connected across the same supply. The current in **B** is 0.5 A. Is the resistance of **A** larger or smaller than the resistance of **B**?
6. Calculate the resistance of a component with a potential difference of 36 V and carrying a current of 5.3 A.

ELECTRICAL CIRCUITS

Rules for series circuit

The diagram shows two components connected in **series** to a battery.

- The **current** in each component is the **same**.
- The total **voltage** across the components is equal to the **sum** of the individual voltages.
- You can apply the equation $V = IR$ to each component.

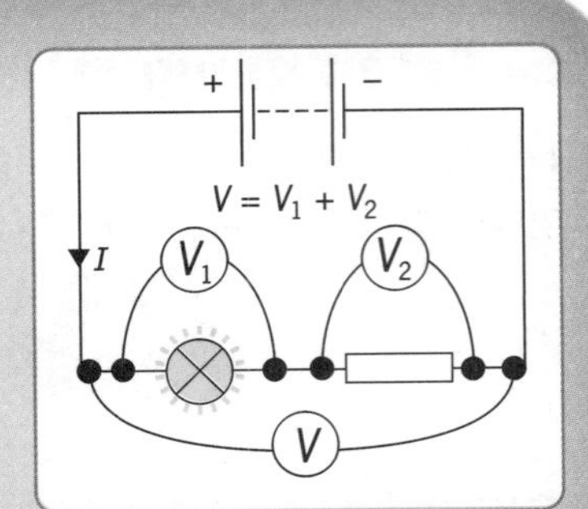

Rules for parallel circuits

The diagram shows two components connected in **parallel** to a battery.

- The **voltage** across each component is the **same**.
- The total **current** entering the **point X** is equal to the **sum** of the individual currents in each component.
- You can apply the equation $V = IR$ to each component.

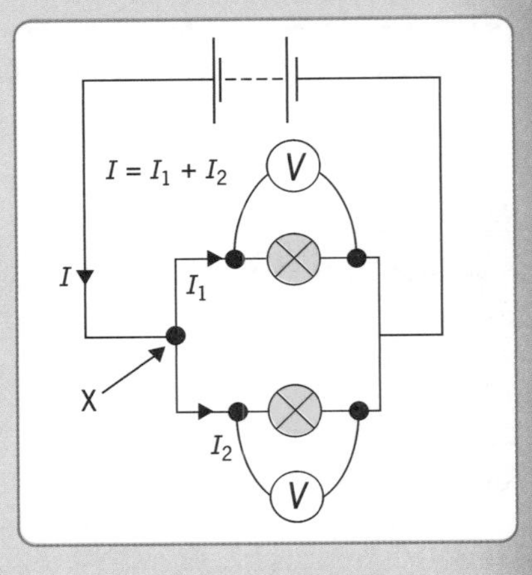

Components in series and in parallel

Series

The total **resistance** of the circuit **increases** as the number of lamps is increased. The circuit **current** will therefore **decrease**.

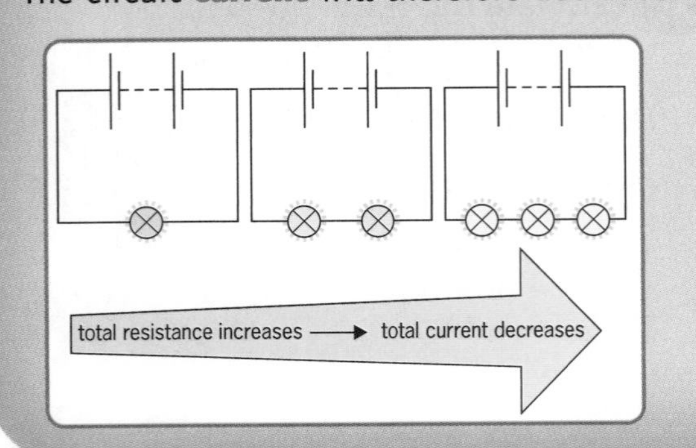

Parallel

The circuit **current increases** as the number of lamps is increased. The total **resistance** of the circuit therefore **decreases**.

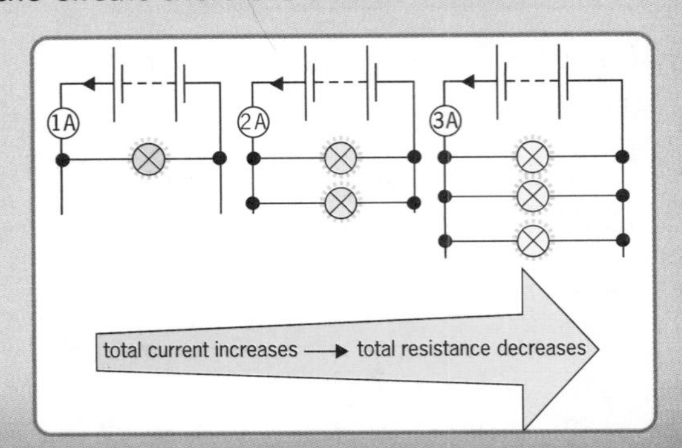

We are surrounded by electrical circuits that automatically do something. The street lights switch on when it gets dark or a warning buzzer sounds if the temperature of a freezer in a shop gets too high.

Light-dependent resistor (LDR)

The resistance of an LDR depends on the amount of light shining on it. The resistance of an LDR decreases as the amount of light falling on it increases:

brighter → lower resistance

A simple 'light-meter' is shown in the diagram.

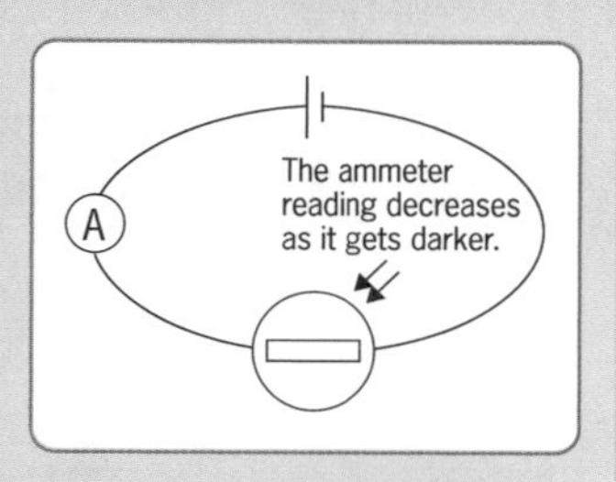

LDRs are used in electronic circuits such as automatic night-lights and burglar alarms.

Thermistor

The resistance of a thermistor depends on its temperature. For a negative temperature coefficient (NTC) thermistor, its resistance decreases as its temperature increases:

hotter → lower resistance

A simple electrical 'thermometer' is shown in the diagram.

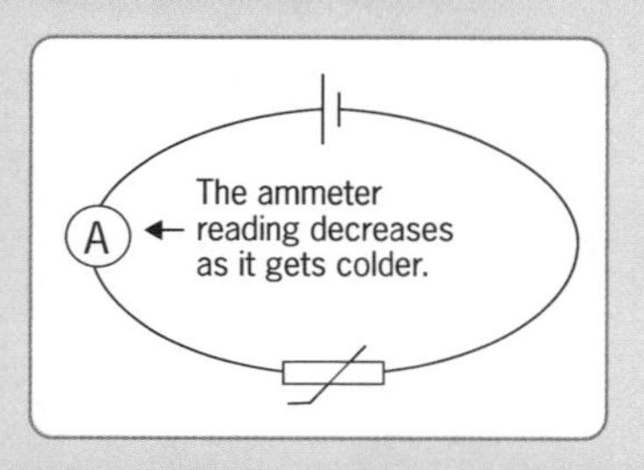

Progress check

1. A resistor is connected in series with a lamp. The current in the lamp is 0.030 A. What is the current in the resistor?
2. What is the same for two components connected in parallel?
3. A lamp is connected to a 12 V supply. Another identical lamp is placed in series with the first lamp. Explain what happens to the current in the circuit.
4. Three filament lamps are connected in parallel to a supply. One of the lamps burns out. What happens to the other lamps?
5. What happens to the resistance of a light-dependent resistor (LDR) in bright light?
6. Name a component for which the resistance depends on its temperature.

ELECTROMAGNETISM AND ELECTROMAGNETIC INDUCTION

Electromagnetism

A current-carrying wire produces a magnetic field around it – this is known as **electromagnetism**.

The magnetic field disappears when the current in the wire is switched off.

The magnetic field lines are concentric circles around the straight wire.

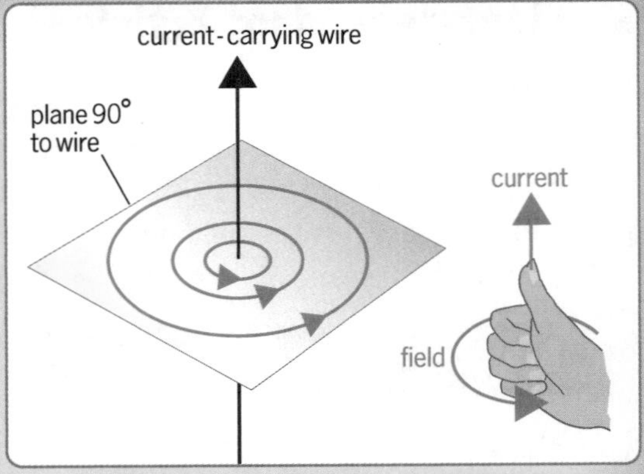

The direction of the magnetic field is given by the **right-hand thumb rule**.

The motor effect

A current-carrying wire experiences a force when placed in a magnetic field – this is known as the **motor effect**.

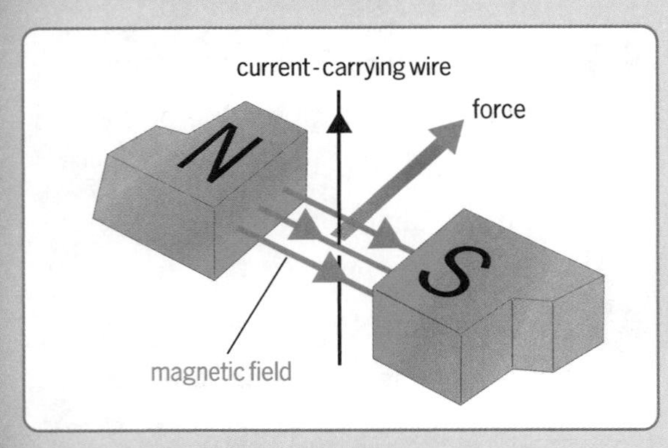

The force experienced by a current-carrying wire is at **right angles** to both the wire and the magnetic field.

The direction of the force experienced by a current-carrying wire in a magnetic field may be determined using **Fleming's left-hand rule**.

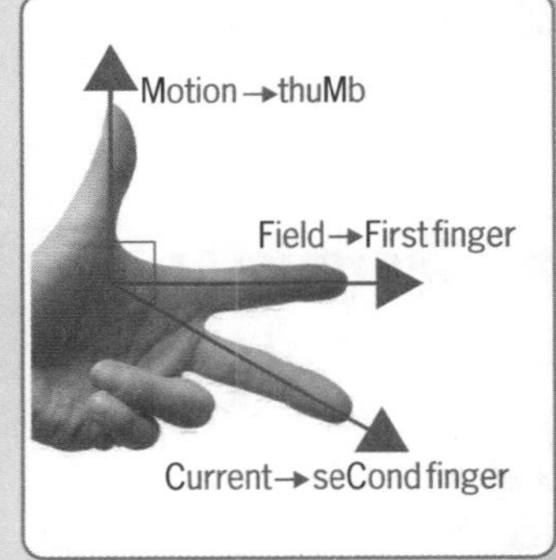

- The **F**irst finger points in the direction of the magnetic **F**ield.
- The se**C**ond finger points in the direction of conventional **C**urrent
- The thu**M**b gives the direction of **M**otion (force) of the current-carrying wire.

Magnets are great fun to play with. Did you know that the electrons spinning within the atoms of the magnet create the magnetic field of the magnet? In fact, all moving charges produce magnetic fields.

Electromagnetic induction

When a magnet is moved close to a conductor or a coil, a voltage is created across the ends of the conductor or the coil. The voltage created in this way is called **induced voltage** and the phenomenon is known as **electromagnetic induction**.

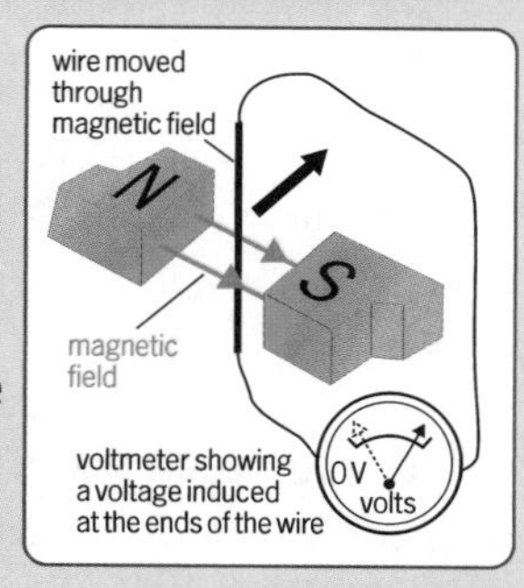

For a **straight wire**, a voltage may be **induced** across its ends by:

- moving the wire at right angles to the magnetic field
- increasing or decreasing the strength of the magnetic field around the wire (e.g. by moving a bar magnet closer or further away from the wire)

Generators

An a.c. generator consists of a coil **spinning** inside a magnetic field.

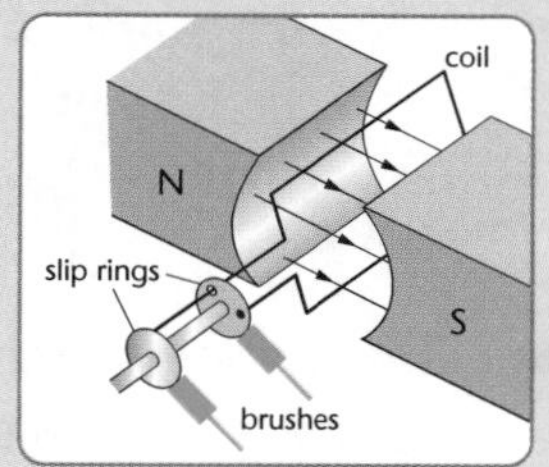

The output from the brushes is an alternating current (a.c.).

Rotating the coil **faster increases** the **frequency** of the a.c. and the size of the induced **current**.

Progress check

1. What is the shape of the magnetic field lines for a current-carrying wire?
2. Name the rule that may be used to determine the direction of the force experienced by a current-carrying wire placed in a magnetic field.
3. What happens across the ends of a wire when it is moved in a magnetic field?
4. The coil of an a.c. generator is spun faster. What will happen to the current generated?

THERMAL ENERGY TRANSFER 1

Conduction

The transfer of thermal energy by conduction mainly takes place in solids.

Thermal energy flows from the **hot** end to the **cold** end of the solid.

In a solid, thermal energy is transferred by **atomic vibrations.**

rods of equal diameter and length covered with wax
cork
hot water
wood
plastic
aluminium
copper
wax melted
good conductors

Metals are very good conductors because they also have **free electrons.** Thermal energy is transferred both by **atomic vibrations** and by **electron diffusion**. Electron diffusion is a much faster process than conduction simply by atomic vibrations.

Metals (copper, aluminium, steel etc.) are good thermal conductors.

Non-metals (plastic, wood etc.) are poor thermal conductors or very good insulators. This is because they have fewer free electrons.

Explanation of electron diffusion

The atoms at the **hot** end have **greater kinetic energy** compared with the atoms at the **cold** end. → The free electrons **collide** with the vibrating atoms at the **hot** end and **gain kinetic energy.** → These free electrons **travel** very fast through the metal and **collide** with the atoms at the **cold** end. → The free electrons **transfer** some of their **kinetic energy** to the atoms at the **cold** end. → The **kinetic energy** of the atoms at the **cold** end **increases.**

Convection

In convection, thermal energy is transferred from one place to another by the actual movement of the liquid or the gas.

Energy transfer by **convection:**

- cannot take place in solids, because the atoms are held rigidly and cannot move over large distances
- can only take place in liquids and gases, because the atoms are free to move over large distances

During hot summers by the coast, have you noticed that sea breeze is always towards the land during the day and towards the sea at night? This is all because of convection currents in the air.

Explanation of convection

As the water is heated at the bottom of the flask, a current of hot water moves upwards and cold water moves downwards to take its place.

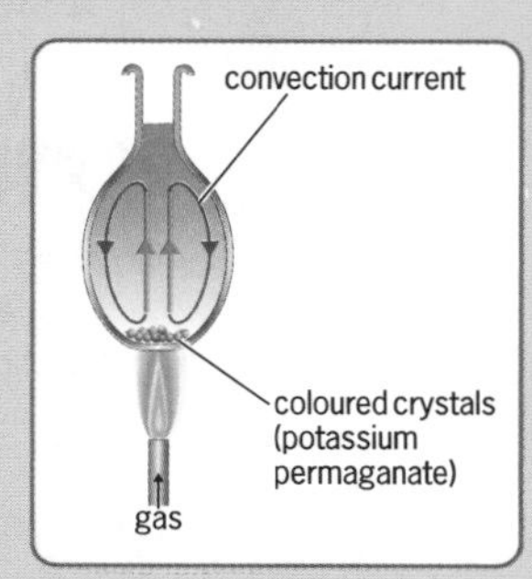

The circular movement of the water is known as a **convection current**.

The heated water at the bottom **expands**.

↓

The water becomes **less dense** and therefore **rises** (just as a cork would do when placed in water or a hot-air balloon would rise in air).

↓

As heat energy is **transferred** to surrounding cooler water, the hot water **cools**.

↓

The **density** of the cooler water **increases** and the water **falls**.

↓

The water gets heated again and the whole cycle **repeats** itself.

Convection in gases

Sea breezes

Convection currents create gentle sea breezes during hot summers.

During the **day-time**:

- The land is hotter than the sea.
- Hot air rises over the land.
- Cooler air from over the sea blows in to take its place (onshore breeze).
- The air in the upper atmosphere blowing in the opposite direction completes the circulation of air.

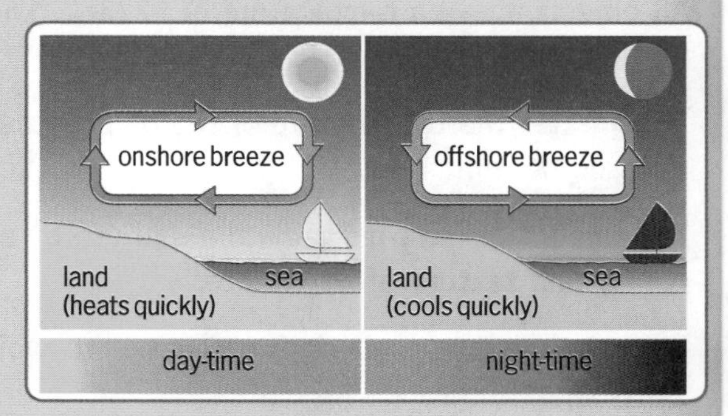

During the **night-time**:

- The land is cooler than the sea because the land is no longer heated by the Sun.
- Hot air rises over the sea.
- Cooler air from over the land blows out to take its place (offshore breeze).
- The air in the upper atmosphere blowing in the opposite direction completes the circulation of air.

THERMAL ENERGY TRANSFER 2

Radiation

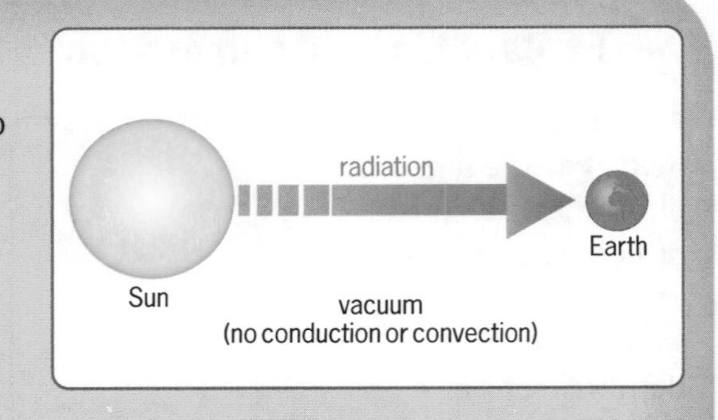

Transfer of thermal energy by **radiation** is due to electromagnetic waves of certain wavelengths known as **infra-red radiation**.

We cannot see infra-red radiation.

Transfer of energy by radiation does **not** require any particles (conduction and convection do!).

Infra-red radiation can travel through a **vacuum**.

The energy from the Sun reaches Earth through vacuum. The energy transfer method must be radiation.

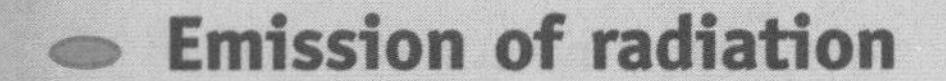

Emission of radiation

All objects above a temperature of −273°C (known as absolute zero) **emit** infra-red radiation.

The **greater** the temperature of the object, the **greater** is the amount of radiation energy released per unit time.

The amount of infra-red radiation emitted by an object in a given time depends on the **colour** and **texture** of its surface.

Objects that have **matt dark** surfaces emit more radiation than identical objects that have **shiny light** surfaces.

Domestic 'radiators' are often painted white. So they do **not** emit a large amount of radiation. If you would like them to emit significantly more radiation, then you should paint them matt black!

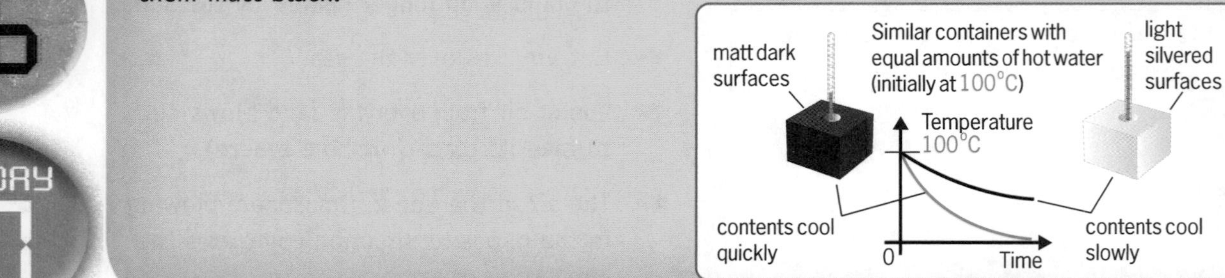

Why are some houses in very hot countries whitewashed or painted in light colours? The houses stay cooler during the day because white surfaces reflect the infra-red radiation from the Sun.

Absorption of radiation

All objects above absolute zero also **absorb** infra-red radiation.

Hotter objects **emit** more infra-red radiation than they absorb from the surroundings.

Cooler objects **absorb** more infra-red radiation from the surroundings than they emit.

Objects with **matt dark** surfaces are **good absorbers** of radiation.

Objects with **light shiny** surfaces are **poor absorbers** of radiation. They are good reflectors of radiation.

silvered
matt black
cork
heater
wax
silver surface → poor absorber
matt black surface → good absorber

Objects with ...	are ...
... matt dark surfaces	**... good emitters and absorbers of radiation**
... light shiny surfaces	**... poor emitters and absorbers of radiation** **... and good reflectors of radiation**

Progress check

1. Which are better thermal conductors, metals or non-metals?

2. In very cold countries, fluffy mammals stay warm and lose less heat by conduction. Explain how this is possible.

3. Why is there no transfer of energy by convection for solids?

4. Convection involves movement of a fluid (gas or liquid). Is this true?

5. Name the waves that can travel through a vacuum and carry thermal energy.

6. Explain why the energy from the Sun cannot arrive at the Earth by either conduction or convection.

7. Many teapots have shiny silver surfaces. Explain why the tea in a shiny silver pot will remain hot for longer.

WAVE PROPERTIES

Waves

There are two categories of wave:

- **longitudinal** waves
- **transverse** waves

For a longitudinal wave, the vibrations are parallel (along) to the direction of travel of the wave.

vibrations

direction of travel

For a transverse wave, the vibrations are perpendicular (right angles) to the direction of travel of the wave.

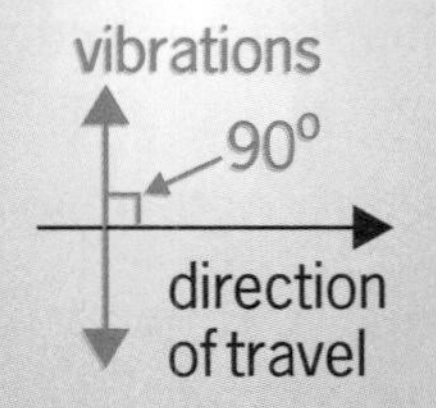

Amplitude, wavelength and frequency of a wave

The **amplitude** A of a wave is the maximum displacement (distance) of a wave from its rest (equilibrium) position.

The **wavelength** λ, (the Greek letter lambda) of a wave is the distance between two neighbouring peaks or troughs.

The **frequency** f of a wave is the number of vibrations per second and is measured in hertz (Hz).

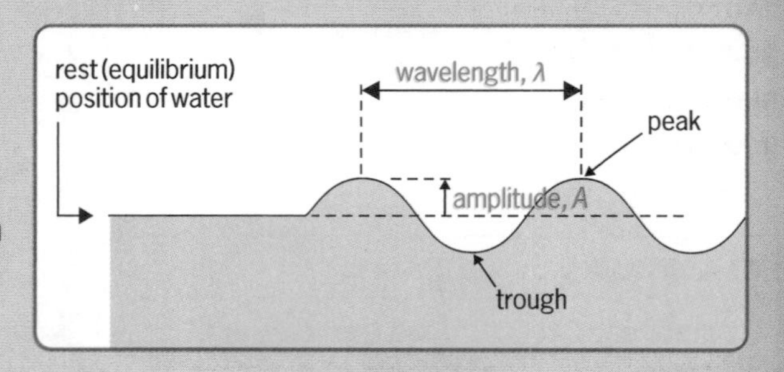

Reflection

When plane waves bounce off a straight (plane) barrier:

angle of incidence = angle of reflection

Why is it that you can hear people talking in a room where the door is slightly opened even though you cannot see them? Sound is diffracted by the small gap in the door but light is only diffracted by a tiny amount.

Refraction

Refraction is the **bending** of a wave as it travels from one material into another.

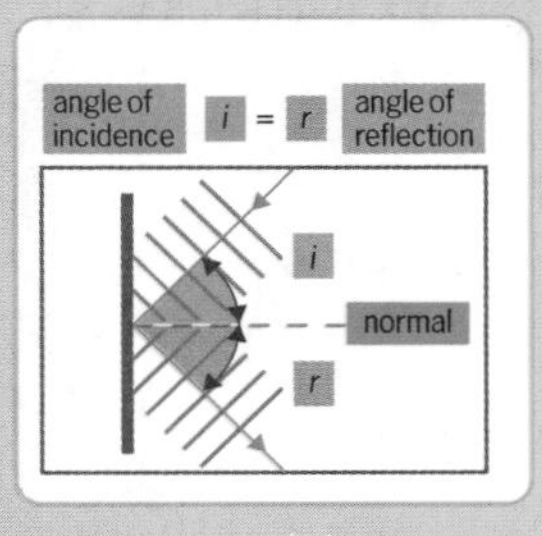

Refraction takes place when the **speed** of the wave **changes** as the wave travels from one material into another (see chapter on light, pages 110–111).

Diffraction

A wave passing through a small gap **spreads** out. This spreading of the wave is known as **diffraction**.

Diffraction is more noticeable when the size of the gap is roughly the same as the wavelength λ of the waves passing through the gap.

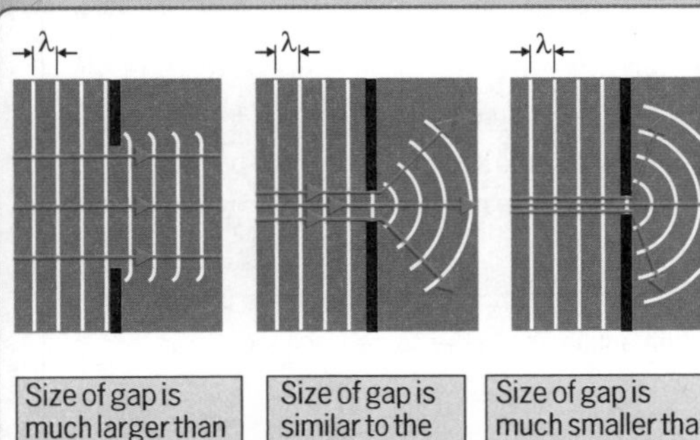

Size of gap is much larger than the wavelength λ. | Size of gap is similar to the wavelength λ. | Size of gap is much smaller than the wavelength λ.

Progress check

1. What is the distance between two neighbouring peaks called?
2. What is the unit of frequency?
3. Light is incident on a plane mirror at an angle of 40° to the normal. What is the angle of reflection?
4. What is refraction?

SOUND

Sound

Sound is a **longitudinal** wave. The **vibrations** of the air particles are **parallel to** (along) the direction of travel of the wave.

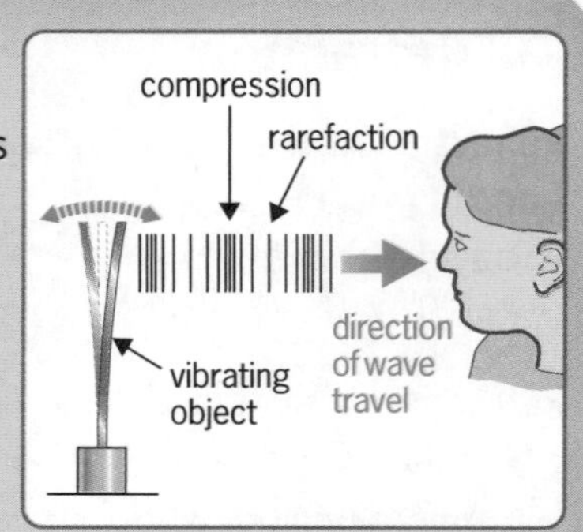

Sound is created by vibrating objects. Sound **cannot** travel through a **vacuum** because there are no particles that can be vibrated. The **speed** of sound in air is about 340 m/s.

The **speed** v of the sound is related to its **wavelength** λ and **frequency** f by the equation:

$$v = f\lambda$$

Frequency and pitch

A normal human can **hear** sound within the frequency range 20 Hz to 20 000 Hz.

The **frequency** of the sound determines the **pitch**.

When the **frequency** of sound is **increased**, a **higher** pitch sound is heard.

When the **frequency** of sound is **decreased**, a **lower** pitch sound is heard.

A microphone connected to a **CRO** (**oscilloscope**) can be used to demonstrate sounds of different pitch.

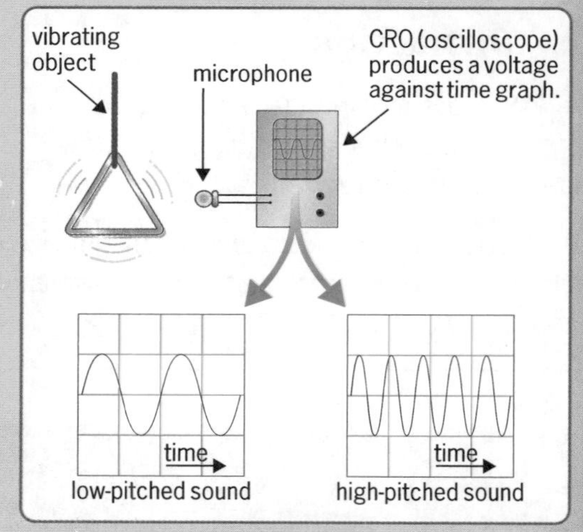

Amplitude and loudness

The **amplitude** of the sound determines its **loudness**.

When the **amplitude** of sound is **increased**, a **louder** sound is heard.

When the **amplitude** of sound is **decreased**, a **quieter** sound is heard.

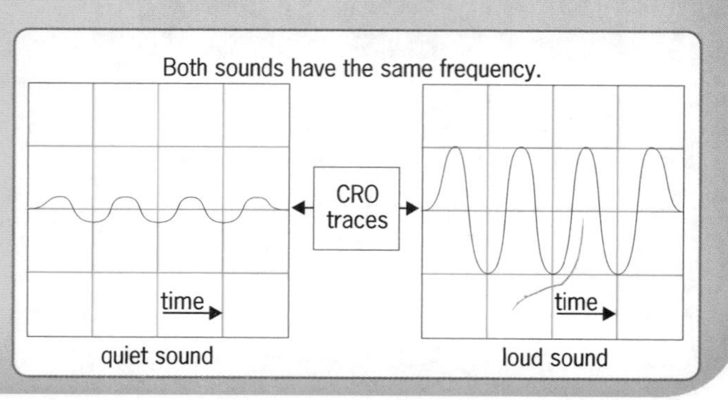

During a thunderstorm, why is it that we see lightning before hearing the sound of thunder? Light travels much faster than sound.

Ultrasound

High-frequency sound that humans **cannot** hear is known as **ultrasound**.

The frequency of ultrasound is greater than 20 000 Hz (20 kHz).

Example

What is the wavelength of an ultrasound of frequency 30 000 Hz? The speed of ultrasound in air is 340 m/s.

$v = f\lambda \qquad \lambda = \frac{v}{f} = \frac{340}{30\,000} \qquad \lambda \approx 0.011\text{ m}$

Echoes

The reflection of sound is known as an **echo**.

Echoes can be used to determine distances.

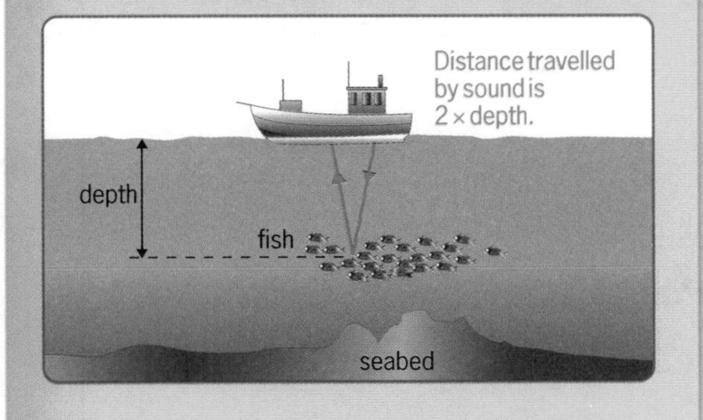

Progess check

1. What do we call the reflection of sound?
2. Explain why sound cannot travel through a vacuum.
3. What determines the loudness of sound?
4. What determines the pitch of sound?
5. Can we hear ultrasound?
6. The highest frequency that a healthy human can hear is 20 kHz. What is the wavelength of sound of this frequency? (The speed of sound in air is 340 m/s.)
7. There is a crack in a metal at a depth of 0.06 m. Ultrasound is reflected by the crack. Calculate the time taken for the ultrasound to be reflected back to the surface of the metal. The speed of ultrasound in the metal is 4000 m/s.

LIGHT

Light

Visible light is part of the **electromagnetic spectrum**. Light is a **tranverse wave** that can travel through a **vacuum** at an incredible speed of **300 000 000 m/s** (3.0×10^8 m/s).

Reflection

When light is **reflected** by a **plane** mirror:

angle of incidence = angle of reflection

$$i = r$$

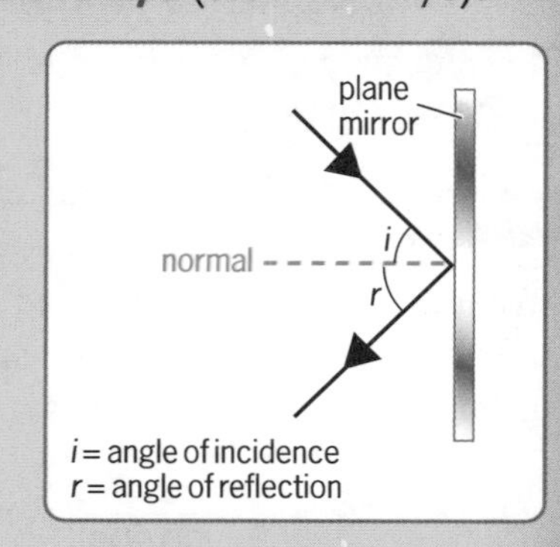

Refraction

Like all waves, light is **refracted** when its **speed changes**.

A ray of light is refracted **towards** the normal when it travels from air into glass or water. This is because its speed **decreases**.

A ray of light is refracted **away from** the normal when it travels from glass or water into air. This is because its speed **increases**.

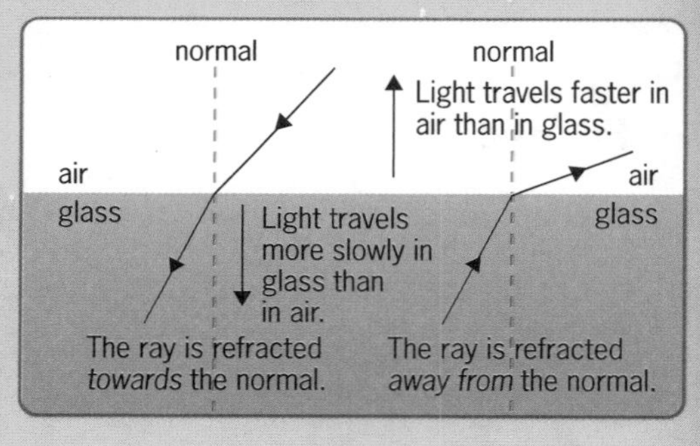

Total internal reflection

What happens to a ray of light travelling through glass when it meets a glass–air boundary?

1 For **small** angles of incidence, the ray is **refracted** away from the normal and there is a weak reflected ray within the glass.

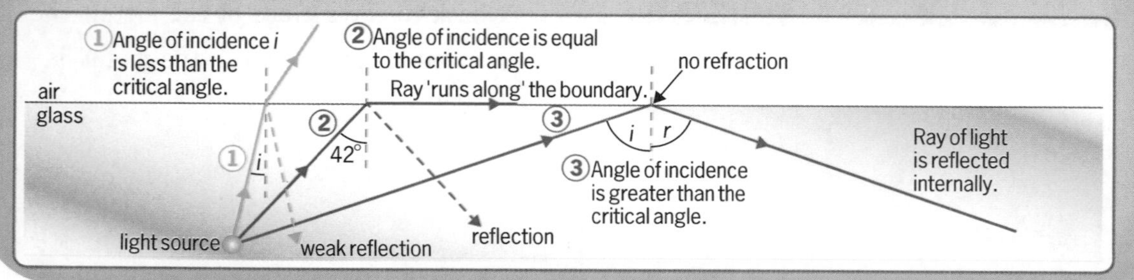

The stars in the night sky emit visible light. Did you know that light from some stars has taken millions of years to reach us?

2 At an angle of incidence known as the **critical angle**, the refracted ray runs **along** the glass–air boundary and there is still a reflected ray within the glass. For glass, the critical angle is about 42°.

3 For angles of incidence **greater** than the critical angle, the light is **totally internally reflected** (there is no refraction).

Applications of total internal reflections

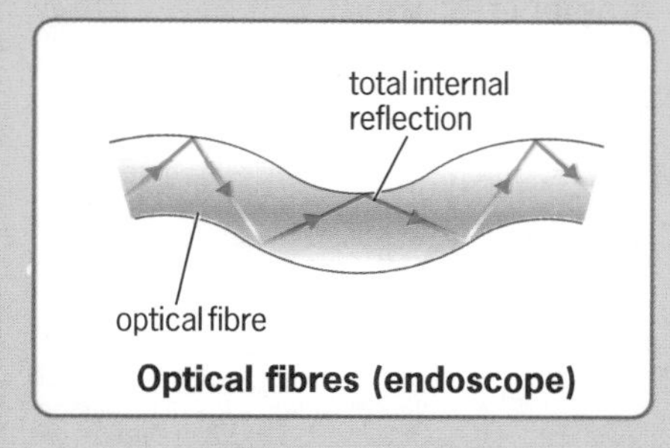

Optical fibres (endoscope)

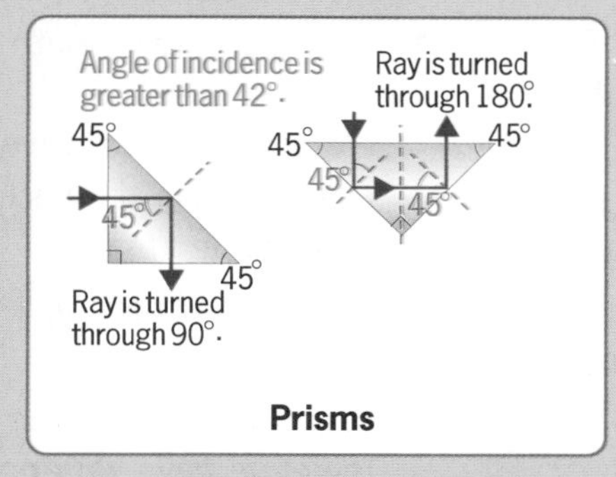

Prisms

DAY 7

RADIOACTIVITY

Radioactivity

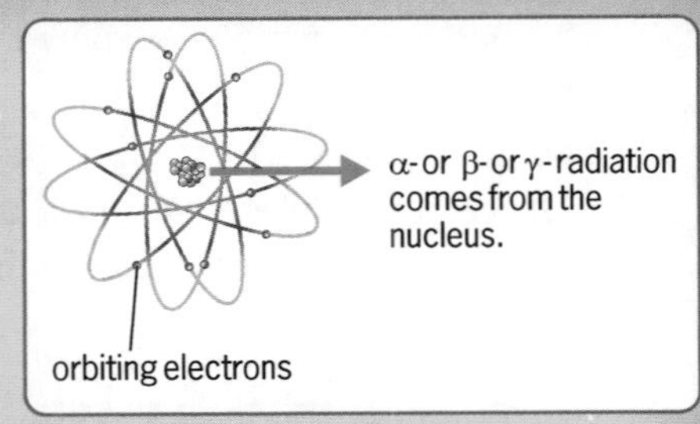

Some substances are naturally radioactive, e.g. uranium.

Radioactivity is related to changes that take place **within the nucleus** of the atoms of a material.

In a radioactive material, the nuclei are **unstable**.

Unstable nuclei become much more stable by emitting radiation in the form of particles (**alpha-particles** or **beta-particles**) or high-frequency electromagnetic waves (**gamma-radiation**).

Dangers of ionising radiation

Radiation from radioactive materials **harms** humans in a number of ways:

- It destroys healthy cells and tissues.
- Over-exposure can lead to **radiation burns** and **cancers**.
- It can change the **structure** of our DNA and hence **affect future generations**.

Properties of α-, β- and γ- radiations

Alpha-radiation (α)

- **Helium nuclei** released from the nuclei of unstable atoms.
- Very good ionisers and therefore have **poor penetration** (absorbed by a few centimetres of air or a thin piece of paper).
- They are **positively** charged.

Beta-radiation (β)

- **Electrons** released from the nuclei of unstable atoms.
- Moderate ionisers and therefore have **good penetration** (absorbed by about a metre of air or thin aluminium sheet).
- They are **negatively** charged.

Gamma-radiation (γ)

- Very short-wavelength (high-frequency) **electromagnetic waves** released from the nuclei of unstable atoms.
- They do **not** have a charge.
- Very poor ionisers and therefore have **very good penetration** (travel through vast distances in air but are stopped by thick sheets of lead).

Is it true that if we handle a radioactive material, we too become radioactive? No. Radioactive materials are dangerous. But we can only become radioactive if the structure of the nuclei in our body is altered!

Uses of radiation

Sterilisation

Gamma-radiation can be used to **kill microbes** in perishable fruits, such as strawberries, in order to keep them fresher for longer.

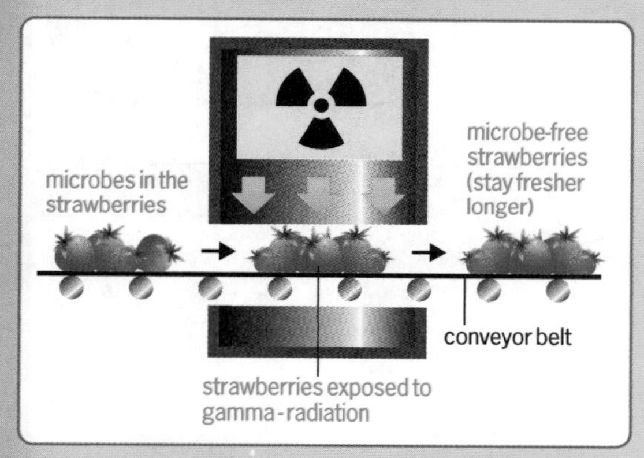

Gamma-radiation is also used to sterilise **surgical instruments**.

Tracers

A **tracer** is a radioactive substance injected into a fluid in order to monitor its flow.

Leaks or blockages in pipes can be determined without the need for digging by using a tracer.

Radiotherapy

Gamma-radiation **kills** both **healthy** and **cancerous** cells.

In radiotherapy, cancerous cells in delicate places like the brain can be killed by carefully aligning **several** gamma-radiation sources.

Progress check

1. Radioactivity is to do with changes that take place within which region of the atom?
2. Name two radiations from radioactive sources that are particles.
3. In what way does radiation from radioactive sources harm humans?
4. Name two uses of gamma-radiation.

THE EARTH'S STRUCTURE AND SEISMIC WAVES

The structure of the Earth

The Earth is not a solid object. It has a **layered** structure.

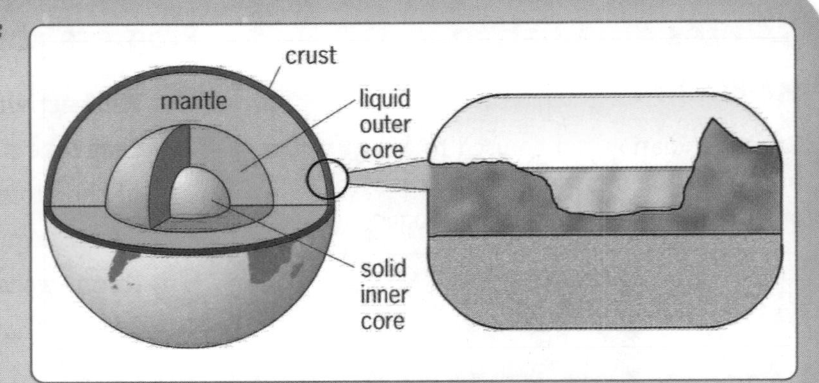

Crust

The outer crust has a **rocky** structure.

Mantle

The upper layers of the mantle have **liquid** properties.

The mantle has fluid properties similar to **hot tar** and therefore allows very slow **convection** currents that transfer energy from the centre to the surface.

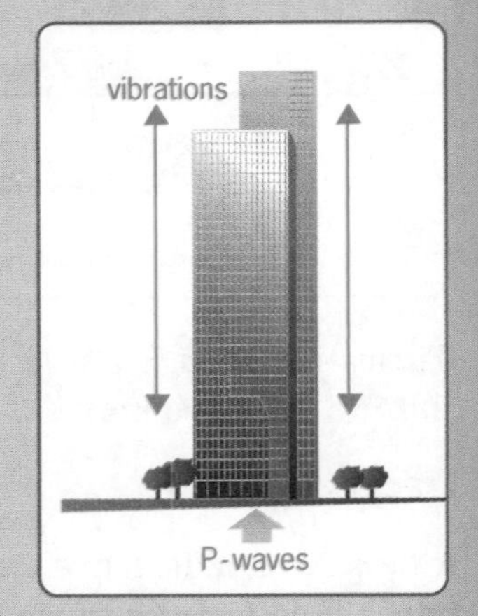

Core

This is made of **iron** and **nickel**. Its **outer** core is **liquid**, and the **inner** core is **solid**.

Seismic waves

An earthquake creates two types of seismic waves:

- primary waves
- secondary waves

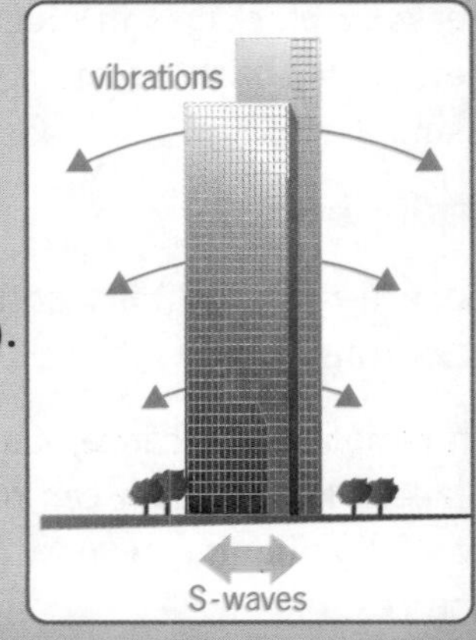

Primary waves

Primary waves (or simply **P-waves**) travel **faster** (at about 10 km/s).

They are **longitudinal** waves.

P-waves **p**ush buildings **up** and down.

P-waves can travel through **solids** and **fluids**.

The catastrophic eruption of volcanoes shows that the Earth is not a solid object throughout, but also has a hot molten interior.

Secondary waves

Secondary waves (or simply **S-waves**) travel much more **slowly** (at around 5 km/s).

They are **transverse** waves.

S-waves **s**hake buildings from **s**ide to **s**ide.

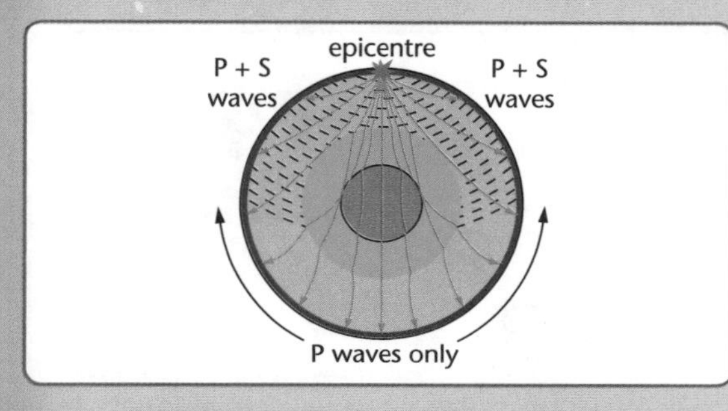

The P-waves travel throughout the structure of the Earth.

The outer core of the Earth stops the S-waves. The **outer core** must therefore be **liquid**.

Within the mantle, both S-waves and P-waves have **curved** paths because of **refraction**. The refraction is due to the **gradual change in the speed** of the waves as they travel through deeper and denser rocks of the mantle.

Progress check

1. What type of wave is the primary or P-wave?
2. Explain why S-waves cannot travel through the Earth's outer core.
3. Name the two metals found within the inner core of the Earth.
4. In the mantle, the paths of both S- and P-waves are curved. This is due to __________.

STARS AND THE UNIVERSE

Life-cycle of a star

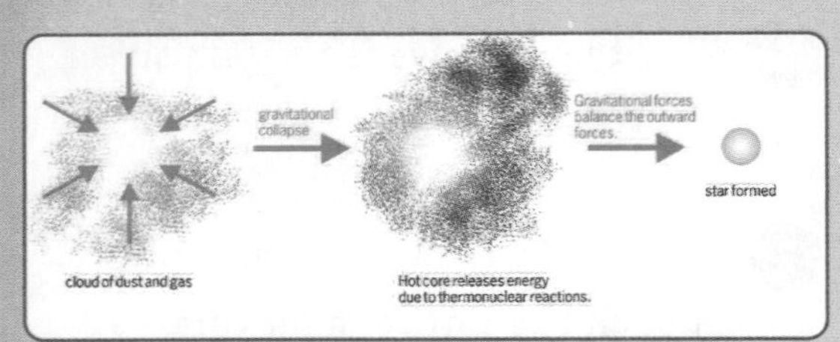

A star starts its life from massive **clouds** of **dust** and **gas** – mainly hydrogen nuclei.

The dust and gas particles attract each other because of the **gravitational force**. The gas and dust cloud **collapses** under the attractive gravitational forces and its temperature starts to increase.

After a very long period of time, the temperature is high enough for **thermonuclear reactions** to occur. This is where hydrogen nuclei join or fuse together to form helium nuclei. This fusion process releases enormous amounts of energy.

The **temperature** of the core of the star **increases**. When the attractive gravitational forces balance the outward forces, the star forms a stable shape.

The fate of the star

For a star like our Sun ...

As the supply of hydrogen runs out, the outer shell of the star starts to expand into a **red giant**.

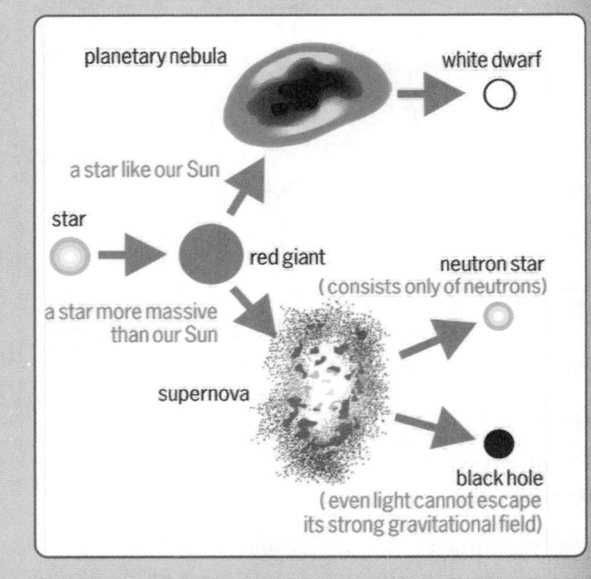

The core of the red giant contracts and the outer shell eventually 'drifts' away into space as a **planetary nebula**.

The core of the star becomes a dense and small star known as a **white dwarf**.

As we look up into the night sky, we see countless stars. All of these belong to our Galaxy – the Milky Way. In the Universe, there are many millions of other galaxies.

The Universe

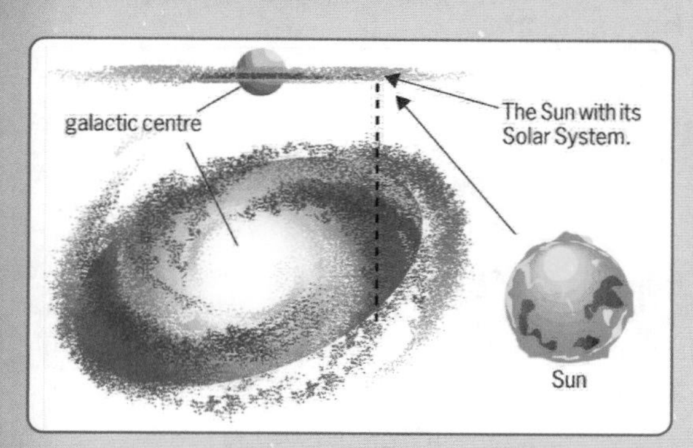

A galaxy consists of **millions of stars** held together by the force of gravity.

Our Galaxy is called the **Milky Way** and is a **spiral** galaxy.

The Universe consists of many **millions of galaxies.**

There is empty space (vacuum) between the galaxies.

All the galaxies are found to be moving **away from** each other.

This is because the whole **Universe** is **expanding**.

ANSWERS

Cells

1 cell membrane, nucleus, cytoplasm
2 cell membrane, nucleus, cytoplasm, sap vacuole, cell wall (Not chloroplasts because root cells cannot receive light under the soil.)
3 nucleus
4 Move backwards and forwards, to move mucus, which has trapped bacteria.
5 Bacteria and pollutants cannot be moved out of the lungs so they build up in the lungs.

Cell action

Statement	Diffusion	Osmosis	Active transport
Molecules move from high to low concentration	✓	✓	×
Molecules move from low to high concentration	×	×	✓
Water molecules move through a partially permeable membrane	×	✓	×
Passage of molecules through a membrane needs energy	×	×	✓
Molecules move down a concentration gradient	✓	✓	×

Photosynthesis

1 carbon dioxide
2 oxygen
3 light, suitable temperature

Human nutrition

1 a) enzyme A
b) pepsin
2 a) enzyme denatured/destroyed
b) inactive

Blood

thrombokinase; prothrombin; fibrinogen

Heart

	Artery	Capillary	Vein
Pressure	50	25	15

Did you make a mistake? Capillaries have a higher pressure than veins. Blood moves down a pressure gradient.

Respiration

1 yeast respiration

Day 1		After 30 days	
yeast	less	yeast	more
glucose	more	glucose	less
alcohol	less	alcohol	more

2 Diaphragm muscles relax, so the diaphragm moves upwards. → External intercostal muscles relax. → Contraction causes rib cage to move downwards and inwards. → Pressure in chest cavity increases. → This causes pressure in lungs to increase. → Atmospheric pressure is now lower than pressure in lungs. → Air flows from the lungs up the trachea and out via the mouth and nose.

Nerves

stimulus → receptor → sensory neurone → axon → dorsal root → spinal cord → synapse → relay neurone→ synapse → motor neurone → muscle. Did you get them all right?

Brain

radial muscle	contracted	relaxed
circular muscle	relaxed	contracted
pupil	big	small
amount of light	lots	little

Kidneys

D	T
Blood linked from an artery to (donor) dialysis machine	Kidney is taken from another person
Dialysis membrane is selectively kidney permeable	Kidney must be matched so that is not rejected
Urea leaves blood	A donor can be living or have recently died
Filtered blood pumped back to a vein	

Homeostasis

Water content in blood too low	**Water content in blood too high**
more ADH	less ADH
more water reabsorbed by kidney	less water reabsorbed by kidney
less water in urine	more water in urine

Inheritance

	b	b
B	Bb	Bb
b	bb	bb

Cell division

1. Metaphase. The chromosomes are at the equator/middle.
2. Five. Each new cell would also have an identical five!

Sexual reproduction

1. testis → sperm duct → prostate gland → urethra → penis → vagina → cervix → uterus → fallopian tube
2. It shows the formation of identical twins. One sperm and one ovum fuse, so the DNA of all cells is identical.

Selective breeding

1. artificial selection
2. No. Sexual reproduction can produce a new combination of features but no new genes. That needs a mutation.
3. People select ones with desirable features.
4. Taken away, used up, not used for breeding.
5. False. The aim is to produce offspring with a better combination of features, but often this is not achieved. You have to try again.

Pollution

As sulphur dioxide increased, so did the death rate. Sulphur dioxide results in acid rain so the fog would have been acidic. This damaged people's lungs, so weaker people with, say, bronchitis, died.

Nitrogen and carbon cycles

No nitrite is formed so no nitrate either. Bacteria Y have nothing to feed from. Ammonia builds up so leaves cannot rot.

Atomic structure

1. b
2. Negligible
3. positive (+1)
4. mass number – 63
   atomic number – 29
5. $^{65}_{63}Cu$

Covalent bonding and structures

1. b
2. simple covalent
3. 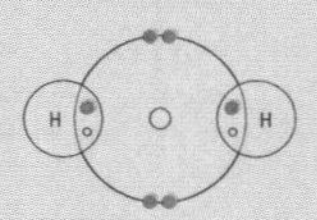

4. Hydrogen chloride is a simple covalent substance and it has a low melting point because there are weak forces between the molecules.

5 Hydrogen chloride does not conduct electricity because there are no free ions or electrons.

6 Diamond and graphite (giant covalent compounds) have high boiling points because there are lots of strong covalent bonds that require a lot of energy to break them.

Crude oil: formation and separation

1 Crude oil was formed by the long term effects of heat and pressure on decaying organic material in the absence of air.

2 A hydrocarbon is a compound containing carbon and hydrogen only.

3 Crude oil is separated by fractional distillation.

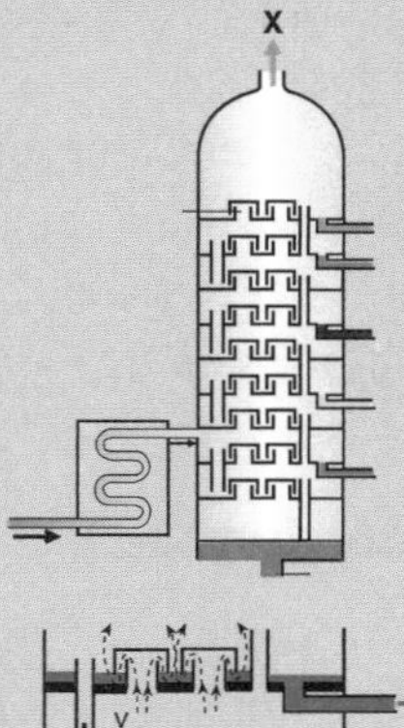

5 Hydrocarbons are separated according to their boiling point (or size of their molecule).

Alkanes and cracking

1 A saturated hydrocarbon is a compound of carbon and hydrogen that does not have any double bonds.

2 C_3H_8

3 ethane

4 heat and a catalyst

5 C_4H_{10}

Alkenes and polymerisation

1 Unsaturated means that there is a double bond between two carbon atoms in a compound.

2

```
H       H
 \     /
  C=C
 /     \
H       H
```

3 By adding bromine water. The octene (alkene) would decolourise it. The octane (alkane) would not.

4 Polymerisation is the process of joining many small molecules containing a double bond (monomers) to form a long chain.

5

```
   H        H        H
   |        |        |
 H-C-H    H-C-H    H-C-H
   |   H    |   H    |   H
   |   |    |   |    |   |
 —C—C—C—C—C—C—
   |   |    |   |    |   |
   H   H    H   H    H   H
```

Copper purification and electrolysis of brine

1 Copper needs to be purified to remove any impurities as these reduce its electrical conductivity (i.e. increase its resistance).

2

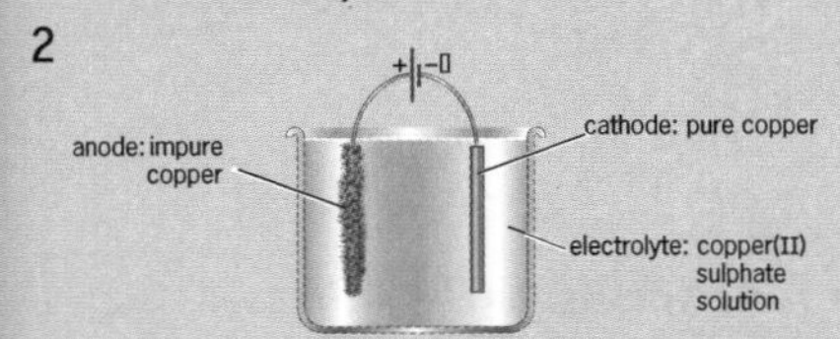

3 $Cu^{2+} + 2e^{-} \rightarrow Cu$

4 hydrogen, chlorine and sodium hydroxide

5 hydrogen – margarine manufacture
chlorine – manufacture of bleach
sodium hydroxide – manufacture of soap

Reversible reactions and production of ammonia

1 A reversible reaction is one that can go forwards and backwards.

2 $\rightleftharpoons$

3 In the manufacture of ammonia a temperature of 450°C and a pressure of 200 atmospheres are used.

4 The temperature is a compromise temperature. A higher temperature would result in a lower yield of ammonia (because a high temperature favours the reverse reaction in an exothermic reaction). A lower temperature would mean that the rate of reaction is too slow to make the process economically viable. A higher pressure than 200 atmospheres would produce more ammonia but it would not be economically viable. It would also significantly increase the risk of an explosion.

5 Ammonia is used to make nitric acid/fertiliser/explosives.

The rock cycle

1 igneous, sedimentary and metamorphic

2 Intrusive igneous rocks have larger crystals than extrusive igneous rocks.

3 The rate at which the rock has cooled and solidified. Intrusive igneous rocks cooled more slowly than extrusive igneous rocks.

4 biological – plant root growth
chemical – acid rain
physical – freeze thaw

5 heat and pressure

Working out formulae

1 Na_2O

2 $MgCl_2$

3 CS_2 (The formula C_2S_4 can be cancelled down to CS_2.)

4 Na_2CO_3

5 $LiNO_3$

6 $Al(OH)_3$

Balancing equations

1 $Ca + O_2 \rightarrow 2CaO$
2 $2Cr + 6HCl \rightarrow 2CrCl_3 + 3H_2$
3 $CH_4 + 4Cl_2 \rightarrow CCl_4 + 4HCl$
4 $4Na + O_2 \rightarrow 2Na_2O$
5 $6P + 3Br_2 \rightarrow 2PBr_3$
6 $4Al + 3O_2 \rightarrow 2Al_2O_3$

Mole calculations 1

1 i. 40
ii. 98
iii. 158
2 i. 40%
ii. 33% (nearest 1%)
iii. 29% (nearest 1%)
3 i. Li_2O
ii. $SiCl_4$

Mole calculations 2

1 13.875 g
2 7.75 g
3 3.18 g
4 2400 cm^3

The periodic table 1 and 2

1 Reactivity increases as you go up the group.
2 Reactivity increases because the atoms get larger, meaning the outermost electron is further away from the nucleus and so it is easier for the atom to lose the outer electron, i.e. more reactive.
3 sodium + water → sodium hydroxide + hydrogen
4 e.g. non-conductors of electricity, low melting/boiling points, brittle/crumbly when solid.
5 i. True
ii. False
iii. False
iv. True
v. False
6 Neon is an unreactive gas because neon atoms have a full outer shell of electrons. This means the atoms do not wish to lose/gain or share any electrons and hence they do not react with any other substance.
7 sodium iodide + bromine → sodium bromide + iodine
8 Bromine is more reactive than iodine because bromine atoms are smaller, hence the outer shell is closer to the nucleus hence it is easier for bromine atoms to gain an extra electron than iodine atoms.

Rates of reaction

1 A sufficient amount of energy called the activation energy.
2 Increasing the temperature means the particles will move more quickly, meaning more collisions, which means more particles will have the activation energy and hence there will be more successful collisions.

3 If the concentration is doubled, then there will be twice as many reactant particles (in the same volume of liquid), hence there should be twice as many collisions and hence the rate of reaction should theoretically double.
4 Smaller marble chips have a greater surface area overall than fewer larger marble chips.

Exothermic and endothermic reactions

1 Exothermic means 'heat is given out'.
2

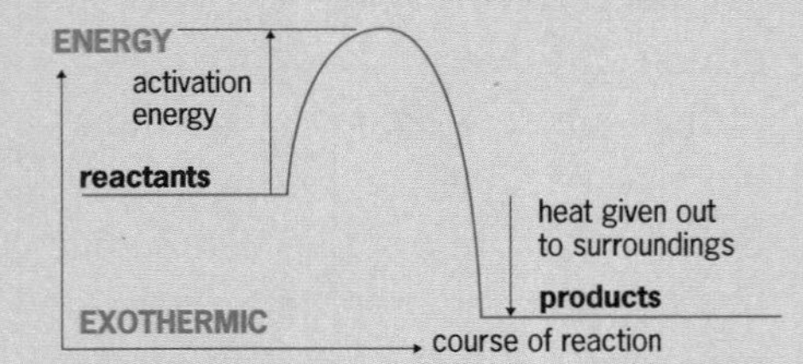

Speed, velocity and acceleration

1 m s^{-1}
2 $t = \frac{d}{v}$
3 0.000 04 m/s or 0.04 cm/s
4 850 m
5 Velocity has direction and speed does not.

Using graphs to describe motion

1 speed
2 acceleration
3 distance travelled along a straight line
4 12.5 m/s
5 100 m

Force and acceleration

1 no
2 net force = 0
3 2.4 N
4 17 N
5 8.5 m/s^2
6 144 N

Friction

1 Friction acts on the object.
2 drag
3 Drag increases.
4 a) acceleration = 0
   b) terminal velocity = 80 km/h
   c) drag = 2100 N
5 No, because the weight is still greater than the drag.

Cars and stopping distances

1 No, it the distance travelled, not time taken.
2 The thinking distance increases.
3 It increases.
4 16 m
5 braking distance = 37 m
(braking time = 3.7 s)
stopping distance = 53 m

Work done, energy and power

1 No work is done because the book does not move.
2 4000 J
3 All the work done is transferred to heat.
4 2800 W
5 240 000 J or 240 kJ

Types of energy

1 Chemical to heat, sound and light.
2 no
3 9.0 J
4 900 J
5 900 J

Static charge and current

1 by rubbing them together
2 electrons
3 amperes (amps or A)
4 yes
5 in series with the resistor
6 1.2 A

Voltage and resistance

1 voltage
2 volts
3 ohms
4 current and voltage
5 **A** has smaller resistance than **B**.
6 6.8 Ω

Electrical circuits

1 0.030 A
2 voltage
3 The current decreases.
4 They remain lit.
5 It decreases.
6 thermistor

Electromagnetism and electromagnetic induction

1 concentric circles
2 Fleming's left-hand rule.
3 A voltage is induced across its ends.
4 The size of the current will increase and its frequency will also increase.

Thermal energy transfer 1 and 2

1. Metals are good conductors.
2. Their furs trap air and air is a poor conductor.
3. The atoms in a solid cannot move.
4. yes
5. infra-red radiation
6. There is a vacuum (no particles) between the Sun and us.
7. Shiny silver surfaces are poor emitters of radiation.

Wave properties

1. wavelength
2. hertz (Hz)
3. 40°
4. The bending of a wave because of change in speed.

Sound

1. An echo.
2. There are no particles (atoms) to transmit the sound.
3. the amplitude
4. the frequency
5. no
6. 0.017 m
7. 0.000 03 s (3.0×10^{-5} s)
   (The distance travelled is 0.12 m.)

Radioactivity

1. the nucleus
2. alpha-particles and beta-particles
3. It damages healthy cells and tissues, cause cancer and alter our DNA
4. radiotherapy and sterilising food

The Earth's structure and seismic waves

1. longitudinal wave
2. S-waves are transverse and these cannot travel in the liquid of the outer core.
3. nickel and iron
4. refraction